Medicine and Humanity

Medicine and Humanity

Edited by Marshall Marinker

 King's Fund

Published by
King's Fund Publishing
11–13 Cavendish Square
London W1G 0AN

© King's Fund 2001

First published 2001

ISBN 1 85717 441 0

A CIP catalogue record for this book is available from the British Library

Available from:
King's Fund Bookshop
11–13 Cavendish Square
London
W1G 0AN

Tel: 020 7307 2591
Fax: 020 7307 2801

Printed and bound in Great Britain

Cover photographs: creativ collection, digitalvision

Contents

Foreword

In 1984, the distinguished Canadian author Robertson Davies gave a lecture to medical students at the Johns Hopkins Medical School in Baltimore, USA, entitled 'Can a doctor be a humanist?' He explained that the Caduceus, or staff, which has been the symbol of the physician for 5000 years, has had two snakes wound around it since the time of the Greeks. These represent knowledge and wisdom. The Greeks recognised that the practice of medicine required both these attributes and depicted their god Hermes using his staff to keep the warring snakes in balance to prevent one devouring the other.

The temptation for knowledge, or science and technology, to overwhelm wisdom or humanity, has never been greater. Of course the advances in biomedical science and technology in the twentieth century are what has made modern medicine effective. The foundation of medical practice has to be based on a sound understanding of science. But if the application of science and technology is not to be dangerous then wisdom is required to determine how and when it should be used. The duty of the clinician is to care and comfort, as well as to treat. When faced with disease and disability the question of what can be done is not always synonymous with what should be done. To answer the question 'What should be done?' requires a deep understanding of the human condition and the particular circumstances of the patient. Medical education must include the opportunity to learn about and understand the needs of people, their families and society. Paramount nowadays is the need to engage with patients as partners, recognising that doctors never save lives, though they can extend them.

There are also questions to be asked about the role of medicine in society, the need to prevent the medicalisation of life, to understand the limits of medicine and to prevent its unthinking application in areas of human behaviour where it is inappropriate.

The idea for the series of lectures and public debates on which this book is based was generated at a meeting called by Mr Dylan Hammond in May 1997. He was organising a festival to celebrate the Millennium, entitled the 'String of Pearls'. He observed that within close proximity of the River Thames, as it weaves its way through London, there are a large number of institutions that have made major contributions to the development of civilisation, and challenged each of these 'pearls' on the string of the River Thames to develop events to celebrate these achievements. Guy's and St Thomas' Hospital in Southwark developed from the monastic foundation of St Mary Overie on the site of the present Southwark

Cathedral. The Very Reverend Colin Slee, the Dean of Southwark and I decided it would therefore be appropriate for the Cathedral and the United Medical and Dental Schools of Guy's and St Thomas' (UMDS) to co-operate in developing the debates on medicine and humanity to be presented in the Cathedral over the year, with an audience drawn from local people and those with a particular interest in the subjects. As our plans developed, so did the merger of UMDS with King's College to form the new Guy's, King's and St Thomas' Medical and Dental Schools (GKT), and the inclusion of King's College into the programme enabled it to be enriched because of the strong background of the humanities within the new college. Indeed, one of the reasons for the merger was to facilitate the introduction of education in the humanities for students of medicine, dentistry, nurses and other health professionals.

In parallel with the richness of the debates that are represented in this book, which has been edited so well by Professor Marshall Marinker, a second important programme was generated. Baroness Genista McIntosh, Chief Executive of the Royal National Theatre, Ms Jenny Harris, Director of Education, and Marshall Marinker developed the notion of a 'theatre of debate'. Responsibility for carrying out this programme was vested in the Y Touring Theatre Company, led by Nigel Townsend, and resulted in a workshop for young people from schools all over the country, held at St Thomas' Hospital. Working with clinicians and medical scientists, theatre directors and writers, these young people went on to create a series of one-act plays in which they reflected their feelings about medical care. Five playwrights were subsequently commissioned to write plays about the ethical dilemmas of modern medicine and these received stage readings at the Royal National Theatre. Plans are afoot for a national tour. This initiative has in turn led to a third outcome of our Medicine and Humanity programme – the creation at GKT of a Chair in Medicine and the Arts, generously funded by the D'Oyly Carte Foundation.

This book, therefore, represents the start of a new initiative to recreate the balance between science and the art of medicine, which has been recognised for so long as the foundation of sound humane practice. I would like to express my gratitude to all the very many people who made this possible, particularly Colin Slee and his staff at the Cathedral, to Marshall Marinker for his ideas and energy, and to Chris Coe and his staff at King's College London for their involvement in the promotion and organisation of the debates. Many were involved, certainly too many to mention by name. The events would not have been possible without the generous support of Merck, Sharpe & Dohme and the Charitable Foundation of Guy's and St Thomas'. We are grateful to Stephen Lustig and the King's Fund for supporting and publishing this book. To the Royal National Theatre and Y Touring, my very special thanks for enabling the larger vision to become a reality. Our hope now is that these ideas will grow and above all that patients will benefit.

Sir Cyril Chantler

References

1. Davies R. *The merry heart: reflections on reading, writing and the world of books.* Harmondsworth: Penguin Books, 1998.

Speakers and panellists

There were six debates during the course of 2000. Two speakers spoke at each debate, and their papers are produced in this book. Following these paired addresses there was a break in the proceedings, during which members of the audience were invited to submit their questions and comments. In a following 'Question Time' session, chaired by Marshall Marinker, these questions were discussed by the speakers, who were joined by other distinguished commentators on the panel.

Health and justice

Speakers

Kenneth Minogue, Professor of Political Science, London School of Economics

Julian Tudor Hart, Visiting Professor of General Practice, University College London

Panellists

Linda Smith, Chair of Lambeth, Southwark and Lewisham Health Authority

Simon Hughes, MP for North Southwark and Bermondsey

Melanie Phillips, Sunday Times columnist and author

Staying human

Speakers

Robert Winston, Professor of Fertility Studies, University of London

Richard Harries, Bishop of Oxford

Panellists

Raymond Tallis, Professor of Geriatric Medicine, Manchester University

Ziauddin Sardar, Visiting Professor of Postcolonial Studies, City University, London

Colin Blakemore, Professor of Physiology, Oxford University

Personal freedom or public health?

Speakers

Bruce Charlton, Lecturer in Psychology, Newcastle School of Medicine

Peter Budetti, Director of the Institute of Public Health, Northwestern University, Chicago

Panellists

Mike Richards, Sainsbury Professor of Palliative Medicine, Guy's, King's and St Thomas' School of Medicine, London

Julia Neuberger, Chief Executive, King's Fund

Martin McKee, London School of Hygiene and Tropical Medicine

Culture, conformity and mental health

Speakers

Jonathan Glover, Professor of Ethics, King's College London

Kay Redfield Jamison, Professor of Psychiatry, Johns Hopkins University, Baltimore

Panellists

Allyson White, non-executive member, Lambeth, Southwark and Lewisham Health Authority

Colin Slee, Provost of Southwark Cathedral

Robin Murray, Professor of Psychiatry, Institute of Psychiatry, London

Living well, dying well

Speakers

Bert Keizer, physician and writer

Rowan Williams, Archbishop of Wales and Bishop of Monmouth

Panellists

Colin Brewer, psychiatrist and writer

Graeme Catto, Vice-Principal and Dean of the Guy's, King's and St Thomas' Hospitals Medical and Dental School

Thurstan Brewin, former Medical Director of Marie Curie Cancer Care, and Chairman of Healthwatch

Health in the city

Speakers

Victor G Rodwin, Professor of Health Policy and Management, New York University

Julian Le Grand, Richard Titmuss Professor of Social Policy, London School of Economics

Panellists

Angela Lennox, general practitioner

Patricia Moberly, Chairman of Guy's and St Thomas' Hospital Trust

Peter Selby, Bishop of Worcester

Chapter 1

The limits of what's human

Marshall Marinker

On words: an introduction

Throughout the year of our Millennium Festival I was privileged to chair the 'Question Time' sessions that followed the six pairs of lectures delivered by our Visiting Millennial Fellows. Subsequently I was invited to edit this book, intended as a legacy of these events. The 12 lectures that follow stand as a testimony to the quality of our speakers' thoughts. What this book does not capture, however, is the quality of the ideas raised in the 'Question Time' sessions, when on each occasion the speakers were joined by three distinguished panellists. In response to comments and questions from our audiences, they and the speakers were able to examine the fine grain of the ethical dilemmas that were raised.

These discussions have proved impossible to summarise, and the verbatim transcripts simply fail to convey the style, pace and intensity of the debates. I have tried to capture something of the scope of them in this opening essay, which, however, remains an entirely personal reflection. I begin this reflection with the basic tools of our deliberations: with words.

In his poem 'Burnt Norton', T S Eliot[1] warns us:

> Words strain,
> Crack and sometimes break, under the burden,
> Under the tension, slip, slide, perish,
> Decay with imprecision, will not stay in place,
> Will not stay still.

Throughout our year-long exploration of the dilemmas that face the individual and society, consequent on what medicine will in future offer, and doctors be able to do, the ambiguity of words was to echo in almost everything said. Terms like 'individual', 'society', 'health' and 'medicine' – the common currency of our debates – simply would not stay in place, would not stay still.

The choice of words in our headline, 'Medicine and Humanity', and in our strapline, 'Millennial Festival of Medicine', was made to challenge us to soar above the immediate problems posed by a struggling NHS. We were, as the word 'millennium' suggests, concerned with grander vistas of time and change. In the event, the hint at a millennial timescape was perhaps a tad ambitious. The historic changes with which for the most part we were concerned might span as much as a century, but it was the decade that proved the commonest currency of our deliberations. And this made sense on a human scale.

Freeman Dyson,[2] in his book *Imagined worlds*, suggests that the decade is the basic unit of historical time – what he calls the 'normal horizon' of human activities – the average life span of a government policy, or of a research programme in science, or of a child growing up. We parcel our personal and social time with such resonant decimal terms as 'The Sixties' or 'The Thatcher Years'. Although our speakers permitted themselves to range far over history, for the most part their purview was limited to little more than a couple of decades on either side of the millennial cusp on which we find ourselves.

Nonetheless, what we were all marking *was* the Millennium. Indeed, the setting for our lectures and debates was Southwark Cathedral – although our participants included members of many faiths, and of none. This setting served well to remind us that the roots of meaning in such words as 'medicine' and 'humanity' were to be found deep in the soil of the Judeo-Christian tradition.

'Medicine and Humanity' signalled the scope and depth of the questions about contemporary medicine that we wished to explore. Inevitably, and out of the direct line of sight of the small group of us who devised this programme, there lurked a host of assumptions, values, propositions and anxieties. Our expressed intention was to create a debate. I do not doubt that we wished also to shape it.

'Humanity', with its attendant semantic burdens of 'humane', 'humanitarian', 'the humanities', and indeed 'humanism', opened out a rich field of enquiry and speculation. In its narrowest sense, humanity suggested only our concern with *human* illness and health, but we clearly intended more than this. The adjective 'human', as the Oxford English Dictionary observes, historically referred not only to matters pertaining to mankind, but carried a distinction from matters divine. Hence perhaps 'humanism' – with its historic enlightenments and dark shadows.

The words 'human' and 'humane' did not express separate meanings until the eighteenth century. The OED lists the character or qualities of being *humane* as:

'behaviour or disposition towards others such as befits a human being – civility, courtesy, politeness, good behaviour; kindness as shown in courteous or friendly acts; obligingness.' The medical profession clearly aspires to be humane: these and similar terms have been imported wholesale into the rhetoric of the General Medical Council's prescription for virtue – *Tomorrow's doctors*.[3]

If 'humane' is an adjective much associated with medical practice, 'humanitarian' is a word increasingly attached to medical aid – especially in the Third World. It gained for itself much approbation at the close of the twentieth century, but there are also question marks about the motivations of the First World in its beneficence towards the Third. Indeed, the term 'humanitarian' was not always so favoured. Again, the OED: 'One … who devotes himself to the welfare of mankind at large; a philanthropist. Nearly always *contemptuous*, connoting one who goes to excess in his humane principles.' This contempt was to echo in some of our discussions about the proper bournes of public health.

Clearly our choice of 'humanity' carried within it contradictions and paradox. 'Medicine' was scarcely a less ambiguous term, needing always to be distinguished from 'health' – a very different concept only tangentially or accidentally connected with what doctors do. As for 'festival', we were to prove less concerned to celebrate the remarkable advances in public health and medical treatment than to fret about what is to come, to warn, to urge caution.

None of this is to complain about our sublime and incomparable English language. Rather, it is to claim that its imprecision is its crowning glory. If in what was to follow we were sometimes to discern a new truth, or see an old truth illuminated anew, the light shone not so much from the words we chose, as from the dazzling spaces between them.

We chose six topics: justice in health and care; the technical limits of human identity; the boundary between the health needs of the individual and the interests of society; the quality of life and the quality of its end; the social and biological meanings of mental health; the challenges to health of urban life. As the year progressed, these different topics echoed with recurring leitmotifs: a note sounded in one would resonate with the chords struck in another, as we strained to catch the moral drift of modern medicine playing in the music of our times.

Health and justice

In our January meeting, fairness was at the heart of the presentations and debate. We asked:

> *Can we achieve equity of access, comprehensiveness and quality (all three) in a publicly funded service? Can we resolve the conflicts between individual entitlement and distributive justice? Can we ever close the health gap between rich and poor? In considering health, what do we mean by justice, equality, equity, needs and deserts?*

Our speakers were sharply divided, with Karl Marx and Adam Smith both prayed in aid of their contrasted approaches. Julian Tudor Hart reflected on a lifetime as a general practitioner serving the needs of a Rhonda Valley once-mining community. He commented: 'Measuring the coping power of poor people against what I thought I could have managed myself, with the same history in the same circumstances, they rarely failed to amaze me.'

Kenneth Minogue presented us with a quite different view: 'Our own society operates on the counter-factual assumption that all its members are capable of managing their own lives. For a great variety of reasons, this is not true.' He concludes: 'We might thus set up, very much against the grain of current thinking, a distinction between the competent and the incompetent members of society.'

Two paths to fairness are thus opened up to us. Hart's proposition, which Minogue was to classify as 'perfectionist', is breathtaking in its ambition. It is no less than the creation, within the NHS, of 'a potentially independent economy and culture, operating within its own entirely new paradigm, with its staff and the populations it serves as its political army'.

Minogue's proposition is more pragmatic. It is to achieve fairness by devoting public funds to the health needs of those whom he denotes as not competent to fend for themselves. In this view, equality is certainly not a precondition of fairness. On the contrary, fairness can only stem from acknowledging the innate nature of all sorts of human inequalities. To do other is to permit doctors to 'follow the Platonic path of telling us how we ought to live'.

For the most part, it was the challenge of achieving justice between the rich and the poor that dominated the debate. Other failures of fair distribution of resources were largely subordinated to this overriding concern. In response to a question about the rights of different groups or individuals, one panellist observed: 'This is a zero sum game – when one wins another loses.' That being agreed, how are we to judge what is just not only between the rich and the poor, but between the old and the young, the mentally and the physically ill, those compliant with medical advice and those who resist it?

Fairness in health care is most often defined in terms of response to health need. Hence Hart's famous postulation of 'The Inverse Care Law'[4] – those in most need receive proportionately the least health resources. One panellist invited us to choose 'between the use of public funds for gender reassignments and hip replacements'. But on which scale are we to measure good or justice here? In the end are not all health needs merely wants in disguise? If that is so, then 'wants' can be described as the wishes of the suffering individual and 'needs' as the wishes of the politically and professionally enfranchised – scarcely a secure basis for fairness.

Fairness has also been discussed in terms of the deserts of the individual. The following question was posed: 'When ill health is self-inflicted – for example in the case of illnesses related to excessive alcohol consumption or cigarette smoking – should people still have a right to free health care?' But can an illness caused by an individual's excessive use of alcohol and tobacco be simply deemed 'self-inflicted'? What alternative forms of gratification might be available to a middle-aged out-of-work quarry worker suffering from obstructive airways disease who is sliding into heart failure? His diseases are closely related to his smoking 40 cigarettes a day, and his many years cutting limestone. What motivation and resources were available to him to help change his behaviour? The notion of culpability in the causes of illness is just too simplistic to provide a safe basis for judgement.

At the close of the nineteenth century Bismarck introduced State-funded health care in Prussia, not out of social idealism (or 'perfectionism') but in order to enhance the productivity of his workers and the fighting efficiency of his soldiery. The notion of health deserts sits comfortably with what has been called the 'commodification' of health care – indeed, with the commodification of health itself. This is no less true because the notion of deserts is for the most part only silently invoked.

Although holding positions at opposite ends of the political spectrum, it seems to me that both Hart and Minogue argue that health care can be justly distributed only when the contract between the individual and the community is just – in all its many social clauses. They would, of course, differ sharply on the definition of such justice. I was left pondering on the monumental expectations that so many of us have of our National Health Service – not only that it be a paradigm of social justice, but that it should become the major means of bringing this about.

Staying human

In March we questioned the technical limits of the human. We proposed the following:

> Bio-engineering may presently offer genetic engineering; xenotransplants; cloning; in vitro pregnancy; gender by design; psychopharmacological control of personality, intelligence, mood, memory and pleasure; motorised prostheses; cosmetic remodelling; nano-engineering; microchip–brain interfaces and so on. How will these possibilities extend, enhance, alter or corrupt the human experience? How can we retain our 'humanity'?

The exploration of the human genome sets the agenda for science today, much as Galileo's cosmology did 400 years ago at the dawn of the Age of Enlightenment. Both speakers and panellists chose genetic manipulation as the exemplar of future change, and this was to tease us about the points at which human life may be said to begin and end.

What seemed to underpin all the contributions to the debate was a shared need to recognise an authenticity in our human identity, and to invoke some ultimate authority for this. Our opening speakers, one a Christian, the other a Jew, and one of our panellists, a Muslim, were able to anchor their thoughts in the authority of God. Early in his address the Bishop of Oxford touched on the role of faith (and its absence) in contemplating *the human*, and sought to establish a broad common ground. 'God does indeed deal with them [matters of life and death], but he deals with them through us human beings'; and 'Three billion years of careful adaptation, its built-in wisdom, suggests that it is sometimes right to go with the grain of nature.' For those of us whose view is not grounded in formal religious beliefs, something like recourse to the notion of 'the grain of nature' provides perhaps a parallel and comforting authenticity and authority.

Are there limits to the technological manipulation of the human, beyond which its subjects will no longer be human? If so, should we attempt to define these limits? Will we be able to ensure that they are observed? Once again we were concerned with the rich diversity of linked meanings embedded in *the human*. I suggest that our hopes for, and fears of, biotechnology are concerned with four fundamental human quests. The first is for certainty; the second, for limits; the third, for perfectibility; the fourth, for adaptability.

First, the quest for certainty. There is a widely held, but erroneous, belief that advancing medical knowledge will reduce uncertainties about what is in store for us;

for example, that genetic testing will be able to tell us the names of our future diseases and the dates of our deaths.

The Bishop appears to concede this possibility, but reassures us that we will not succumb to its gloomy consequences: 'I wish to challenge the view that this vast increase in knowledge, leading to certainty in so many spheres where in the past there had been only uncertainty, will lead to fatalism. The human spirit is not made like that.' This fatalism would also be misplaced on scientific grounds. Our genetic codes predict a host of likelihoods and vulnerabilities. But the expression of our genetic material as our human selves (what our genetic material becomes) depends on uncountable interactions between the different components of that genetic code and a host of environmental accidents – physical, psychological and social. Genetic science will not shift us from the present age of probabilistic medicine to a future state of fully predictive medicine.

I think the news here is good. It looks as though genetic medicine will give us the best of both worlds. We will have greater potential for intervening effectively at very early stages in many presently destructive diseases, but we will *not* be burdened with certainty. The views from science and religion seem here to be in step. Lord Winston rejected the possibility of scientific certainty, not only on the ground of his insights as a scientist, but on what seemed the ground of faith: 'If we are determined by our genes then free will no longer exists – I don't think this is the case.'

One member of the audience posed the following question: 'When it becomes possible to determine one's medical future, will the panellists take the opportunity of benefiting from this? Should we follow suit?' Somehow no panellist managed to respond directly, which I found the most telling of answers.

Second, we were concerned with the quest for our natural boundaries – for limits. We tend to think of boundaries as external to us – for example, the 'edges' of our bodies, our families, our communities, our personal, social and political environments. The emergence of genomic medicine turns our attention to the boundary on the inside – to the make-up of our genotype.

Throughout the discussion of all our six topics, we returned to the nature of the individual human life – to the internal boundary of the self and the external boundary with others. In a poem called 'On not saying everything', the poet Cecil Day-Lewis[5] writes of the essential need for boundaries – in the growth of a tree, of a poem, of a love affair:

So wanting to be all in all
And each for each, a man and woman
Defy the limits of what's human.
But when we cease to be explorers
And become settlers, clear before us
Lies the next need – to redefine
The boundary between yours and mine.

The Bishop of Oxford echoed these sentiments when he said: 'A sculptor works with a particular piece of stone, a painter with a specific canvas. It is in wrestling with the particular, with quite specific constraints and definite boundaries, that art is produced. The same is true of life … Constraints, boundaries, limits can all act to liberate the potential we have within us to be truly human.'

Our genotypes have not hitherto been purposively self-constructed, even though we may allow the selective breeding of cattle, horses and dogs to have been the forerunners of contemporary genetic manipulation. Until now, the human has seen the internal boundary of the self as determined by God, nature or chance. But how will we feel about our identities, our very selves, when these have been determined by parents, bioscientists, philosophers and governments? One member of the audience conjured up a vision of future family law, under which a child might sue his parents for failure to eliminate an undesired genetic characteristic.

Third, we came to look at the quest for perfectibility. Lord Winston noted a number of hazards in this drive to improve the stock: 'We already live in an unequal society. With enhancement we would have a superhuman group and further inequality. Putting something into our children, something we think subjectively to be good, might prove not to be objectively good.'

The biological, as distinct from the moral, impediment to genetic perfectionism is the false notion of the 'bad' gene. Why have so-called bad genes (for example those associated with schizophrenia or breast cancer) survived? Was it incompetent of natural selection to have permitted the perpetuation of these saboteurs of our genetic success?

There are two biological explanations. First, it seems that many of the genes that make us vulnerable now to diseases in old age, convey benefit earlier in life. We have simply not been programmed for the current human life span in the developed world. Second, so-called bad genes may well have conveyed positive benefit early in our evolution. A gene that contributes to a propensity to obesity today (associated with diabetes and heart disease) may have served our primitive forebears well through hard winters or in times of famine. To eliminate them now from the human repertoire might prove to be a costly mistake.

What of the moral objection to the quest for human perfectionism? There was something chilling in the idea of genetic medicine enhancing our humanity; an echo of that ancient Hellenic ideal which is widely held to have provided the inspiration and model for Nazi idealism. This may have begun for many of its adherents as a seemingly innocent longing for health, beauty and purity of body, heart and spirit, but it ended in the death camps of Treblinka and the rest.

Lord Winston took a more robust view of the dangers: 'We have always practised eugenics. Orthodox Jews, Muslims, Christians will marry one of their own and have children. It is foolish to think this will lead to a Nazi society, and nonsense to think we are trying to create a perfect baby – we can only prevent a baby having a particular disease. *It is the degree to which you practise all these things that matters.*'

Describing transgenic technology as the single most valuable biomedical advance in recent years, Winston raised the future possibility of using the appropriate transgene to immunise an entire population against a fearfully destructive disease – he gave the example of beta-thalassaemia among Cypriot children. He was making the point that by altering the germ line, the future children of those treated would in fact be transgenic.

This technical fix, the 'repair' of a continuously ravaged population, seems morally safe, but raises another qualm about the spiritual consequences of perfectibility. Take the example of Down's Syndrome. Would the elimination of this condition by whatever biomechanical means be desirable? And by whom? And by what utilitarian criteria? Such questions, I suggest, force us to consider whether a fully 'healthy' society, in biological terms, can ever be fully human.

Fourth, it seemed to me that the human quest to adapt was least touched upon in our deliberations. The last time that the genome of homo sapiens was subjected to the cold chisel of Darwinian natural selection, we were hunter-gatherers on the savannah. Will we now be able to use bioscience for politically purposive adaptations?

The Bishop referred to an old rabbinical distinction between repairing and enhancing the universe. This distinction may help us to unravel the intentions and consequences of twenty-first century medicine as it is employed to enhance our human characteristics in a variety of ways that are only tangentially related to the avoidance, amelioration or cure of illness.

In the foreseeable future, our mood, memory and intelligence may all be promoted by a psychopharmacology based on a deeper analysis of brain function. Mechanical prostheses have already been activated by neural impulses, and medical physicists have speculated about direct microchip–brain interfaces. Surgery and pharmacology can now offer a reassignment of gender. Homo sapiens may thus come to be replaced by 'Designer Man'. And the very term 'Man' will no longer call forth feminist ire. 'Man' will be inappropriate once we are freed from the limited choice between only two genders. None of these biotechnical wizardries seemed yet to engage our speakers, panellists and participants.

We were left with some shadows of foreboding about the future integrity of our humanity. The potential of twenty-first century medicine to intervene ever more powerfully in our lives, and to extend its burgeoning technologies into new territory, brings anxiety in equal measure with hope. One of our audience, a Minister of Health in the last government, commented and asked: The Bishop of Oxford believes that 'not everything that could be done should be done'. In a global economy, how can regulation be agreed and enforced? The uncertain answers left us very worried indeed.

Personal freedom or public health?

In April our concerns about health and care turned to the boundary between the State and the individual. We asked:

> Can we have public health and personal freedom? Can we reconcile personal entitlement and public responsibility? Will healthy living (including behaviour modification and screening) become enforceable by law, and with what consequences? What should we expect of doctors in the future? What should we expect of citizens?

As I write this, important news on progress in the Human Genome Project has just been published. It appears, to the surprise of the scientists, that the human genome is made up of some 30,000 genes – a mere third of the widely predicted number. Two insights follow. First, our genetic make-up is disturbingly far more like that of the mouse than we had thought possible. Second, and more pertinently, the role of our environments in shaping the expression of our genes, in determining the way in which the individual human develops, is infinitely greater than we had believed. The effect of environments and human behaviour on the incidence of diseases has traditionally been the concern of public health. So has the control of both in the pursuit of health.

The public health movement in Europe grew out of seventeenth- and eighteenth-century mercantilism. In this tradition, concern was for the health of the nation State. The individual was simply the basic unit of the State, that part of the State which cannot be divided further. The meanings that we now attach to the term 'individual', which refer to autonomy, privacy, liberty, entitlements and so on, are relatively recent. In earlier centuries, health, far from being a right, was rather a duty. It was the duty of the subject to preserve his health in the interest of the State, and it was the policy of the State to help him do so.

Bruce Charlton, our first speaker, was concerned with the intrusion of the State on personal freedom, and took the regulation of psychotropic medicines as his exemplar. It was the complicity of the State in promoting an unwholesome aversion to risk that was his prime target: 'from the public health perspective psychiatry has the puritanical tendency to sacrifice individual happiness, fulfilment and creativity whenever this sacrifice contributes to the goals of preventing harm.' In this mental health context he set a wider argument about the tendency of government to intervene in other areas of our life and behaviour. To what extent does this go beyond what is necessary to ensure sufficient public safety? And on what scale are we to measure this sufficiency?

Peter Budetti, Director of the Institute of Public Health, Northwestern University, put the case for *more* involvement of government in matters concerning health than was current in his own country, the USA. It was almost startling to be reminded by him that in America today, such are the libertarian sensitivities that proposals to institute a national system of universal health care have been opposed on the ground that such a system would constitute an infringement of personal freedom.

Charlton is concerned, wherever possible, to roll back the tide of government interference in the private life of its citizens. Budetti deconstructs this private life to argue that since no individual functions other than as a part of society, there must be a collective will and authority to impose on each individual such infringements of liberty as are necessary to sustain that society. At the heart of the debate, I believe we were considering the notion of risk – but from a number of conflictual perspectives. Charlton takes the case of antidepressant drugs, and argues that there is no good reason to deny citizens free access to them, unburdened by any endorsement from a doctor. He notes that the use of alcohol can be destructive of health, but that it also conveys great benefit to the majority of us. However, as a matter of history and convention in the UK, we do not classify alcohol as a psychotropic drug, and so do not seek to minimise the risks of drinking by medical control.

In defence of personal freedom, Charlton intriguingly asserts that 'subjective experience is more important than objective statistics'. I would argue that his position does not need such defence, in fact it weakens his argument. The sense we try to make of numerate data is no less subjective than the sense we try to make of our experience. Both must always be subject to individual history, attitudes and personality, that is to say 'contingent' and 'subjective'. In this sense, all calculations of risk are obscured, rather than illuminated, by the presentation of health statistics as 'objective'. In this context, the use of 'subjective' as a pejorative diminishes the whole human experience.

Public health is essentially a political, before it is a scientific, endeavour. Hence, it must always take a collective, in this sense an abstract, view of health risk. This risk can only be expressed as averages and will always be at variance with the view taken by any of the unique individuals in the population. It is the *population* whose general or common health the public health project is aiming to protect and enhance.

Most of our data on health risk, whether we are considering the prognosis in a particular sort of cancer, or the damage from cigarette smoking, or harm from the 'unwanted effects' of effective medicines, are statements about groups, populations of people. The data describe an average experience of people in that population. They reveal nothing about the actual chances of any individual. Public health, therefore, in addressing the problem of risk avoidance in groups, inevitably infringes the liberty of individuals who may not themselves actually be at risk, or who are not personally risk averse. Our appetite for paying for this public health in the currency of personal freedom is, therefore, analogous to our appetite for paying taxes. It will all depend on how much we are invited to pay, and for precisely what purposes.

Just as there is moral hazard in confusing absolute with relative risk, so there is hazard in confusing associative and causative factors in disease. For example, in the case of coronary heart disease, we know that such factors as obesity, high salt intake, a cholesterol-rich diet, and a sedentary life, interact with each other, with environmental situations, and with the patients genetic make-up, in a very complex way. This stops short of constituting a description of cause. On this ground, much of the preventive medicine campaigns have been mocked in the name of robust scientific scepticism.

The scepticism is valuable. But I am unconvinced that it rocks the boat of 'preventive medicine' quite as dramatically as the sceptics suggest. Public health medicine is engaged in the attempt to change the behaviour of populations in order to confer benefit on unknowable individuals in that population. The proposition is that I purchase the better health of unknowable others at the cost of elements of my own freedom. Since I hold that man is a social being, I think the price fair, and do not even need to be reassured that one of the beneficiaries may well be myself.

But there is another political critique, and a telling one. McCormick[6] points out that while we disdain the risks to health of those who smoke three packs a day and dine on hamburgers and chips, we 'admire those who take approved risks – racing drivers, trapeze artists, mountain climbers'. He writes of 'a new and growing health fascism'. Charlton quotes, with approval, Gerald Klerman's reference to 'pharmacological Calvinism'. Petr Skrabnek[7] coined the term 'coercive health'. The language of these commentators suggests passion, fear and anger. I am left with questions unanswered. Yes, I hold freedom more dear than health. But what sort of freedom is available to those whose health has been forfeit?

Budetti breathtakingly shifts the debate about health preservation and personal freedom, to concerns about planetary survival. He notes that 'global development is largely seen as degrading the environment in ways that will diminish health' and concludes that 'measures to protect the public's health necessarily involve constraints on economic development'.

In the NHS we are constantly arguing for greater resources to fund our burgeoning appetite for high-quality health care. This seems to be contingent on a steady growth in our private and public wealth. Yet Budetti warns us of the cost of such growth – a cost that may first be paid by the Third World, and eventually by us all in an unsustainable global environment. Such warnings are hard to hear against the general clamour in our First World for 'progress'.

This global perspective provokes us to ask uncomfortable questions about the boundary of our concern. Instinctually we begin with family, and extend our circle of commitment to our friends and neighbours, perhaps to our local communities. But how far does this extend? It was perhaps with such a question in mind that Margaret Thatcher, the prime minister who gave her name to the libertarian tendency in British politics in the 1980s, famously asserted that there is no such thing as 'Society'. The perspective of public health suggests that there is no such thing as the unconnected individual. However counter-instinctual, in the shrinking world of the new millennium the lines of our connectedness stretch far beyond the home, parish or nation. The insights of medical science demonstrate that to be fully human, to be healthy, we must connect and co-operate – that we can only function as part of a society, and that the health of one cannot be pursued separately from the pursuit of health for all.

Culture, conformity and mental health

In June we asked:

> *Who defines mental health; what are our values and goals? What are the links between mental health and crime? What causes, preventive measures, and treatments of mental illness are suggested by conflicting theories from medicine, psychology, anthropology and criminology?*

It could be argued that it was only in the final years of the twentieth century that psychiatry came to be grounded in medicine's science. Insights from recent techniques of brain imagery and the genome project have begun to suggest the anatomical and biochemical locations of our feelings and behaviours. To date, psychiatric diagnosis has been largely an empirical and phenomenological exercise. The doctor observes behaviours and elicits thoughts and feelings from which he deduces a diagnosis.

There have been brave attempts to standardise these procedures – for example, indices of 'depression' or 'anxiety' or 'dangerousness' based on the responses to questionnaires. The intention here is to minimise the role of the doctors' perceptions, choices, prejudices. Psychiatry still awaits the twenty-first century equivalents of those biochemical tests, electronic tracings and three-dimensional images that currently grace our diagnoses of heart disease and the like. I would argue that much more than in heart disease, psychiatric diagnosis depends on something as hard to pin down as 'feel', 'experience', 'clinical judgement'. In fact, there is good evidence that the ascription of psychiatric diagnoses by both general practitioners and psychiatrists is a pretty hit-and-miss affair.[8] This is not to say that the quality of the treatment of these patients necessarily suffers from this diagnostic anarchy – only that there is diagnostic anarchy.

It was these uncertainties – the mixed clinical and political nature of psychiatric diagnosis – that lay behind many of the questions posed for this event. Jonathan Glover, a philosopher with a particular interest in the nature of human identity and the ethics of mental health, focused on the social and legal control of people deemed to be dangerous. Such people are variously described as 'psychopathic' or suffering from a 'severe anti-social personality disorder'. He spoke against a background of current concern about the Government's proposal to detain such people compulsorily, not on the hitherto firm ground that they had committed an offence, but on the uncertain ground of their estimated propensity for harmful behaviour. A key problem is that the instruments developed to assess the dangerousness of individuals are imperfect.

Glover quotes the following figures and poses some hard questions. Of 300 people detained under the proposed arrangements, 200 would have gone on seriously to harm others. One hundred would not. Glover asks: 'Is this margin of error acceptable when people's liberties are at stake?'

Earlier I had invited Jonathan Glover to hold an ethics seminar for a group of academics and professionals who were researching these problems. Playing one of the mind games that philosophers love to employ, he invited us to say which of the following two interviews we would least wish to have to conduct. The first was with a man detained in a mental institution for more than half a lifetime, on the ground of potential 'dangerousness'; in fact, he would have harmed no one had he lived free. The second was with the mother of a child who has been savagely beaten and raped by a man whose test results had suggested this danger. But, in the name of the sanctity of civil liberty, he had not been detained. The choice before government is a policy that takes public safety as an overriding priority, or one that puts civil liberty first. Either policy (for safety or liberty) must comprehend one of these two ruined lives.

I found another of Glover's use of statistics arresting. The Government's proposals for a preventive detention policy will avoid 200 of the 57,000 violent crimes committed each year. A reduction of the urban speed limit from 30 mph to 20 mph would reduce the deaths of children hit by cars from some 50 per cent to 5 per cent. He argues that a speed limit of 20 mph 'would avoid far more death and injury than the Government's psychiatric proposals'.

Once again, as so often in deliberations about the ethical dilemmas posed by medicine, the data may suggest answers in terms of populations, but are silent when it comes to the specifics of individual chances and choices. Even the proposed mind games elucidate only our individual fears and prejudices.

Glover reminds us that all research into the natural histories of violent and dangerous people reveal that they themselves were victims of aggression earlier in their lives – and almost always of their own dysfunctional families.

It was an imaginative stroke to give us, at first under some disguise, the family history of Adolph Hitler. Imaginative because it seemed to explain a great deal about his make-up, and in a chilling way I found that it certainly made him recognisably human. Evil, of course, is a concept from religion, not science. Yet it is hard to contemplate the behaviour of those described as suffering from a severe anti-social personality disorder, without challenging the science that offers us the language of the damaged personality, in preference to the religious concept of evil.

Nonetheless, I passionately hold that the language of mental illness in respect of those with severely disordered personality is superior to the language of crime and punishment – despite psychiatry's relative clinical impotence in the field. A medical diagnosis offers the hope of change, while, for the greater part, prison offers only punishment and containment. Society and victims have just cause to wish to punish those who have harmed them, and society needs to be substantially protected from their threat. But without the hope of treatment, even when treatment seems a distant hope, the otherwise purposeless containment of the inhumane threatens our own humanity.

Michel Foucault[9] traces the modern European hospital to its roots in the medieval Lazar houses. As leprosy receded southward, these lazar houses became vacant. By the eighteenth century they were being transformed into the lunatic asylums. The non-conformism of the mad, who had previously had a recognised place in communities, became increasingly irksome to those creating the orderly machineries of State. Foucault describes this as the 'great containment'. This link between politics and the perception of mental illness surfaced when one of the panellists offered the following:

Schizophrenia among UK resident Afro-Caribbeans is in fact six times higher than among rest of population. But this is not true when Afro-Caribbeans live in the Caribbean. The high UK schizophrenia levels are therefore linked to the experience of being black and living in the UK – a society still generally perceived as racist by Afro-Caribbeans living here.

In fact, the propensity of an indigenous psychiatric culture in the UK to label Afro-Caribbean's as 'schizophrenic' is reversed when it comes to the diagnosis of severe anti-social personality disorder. Surveys of special hospitals and prisons suggest that where a person with severe anti-social personality disorder ends up in the system cannot be predicted on the grounds of the severity of the crime or the dysfunction of the offender. Unconscious racial stereotyping may be at work.

Another contributor offered us this:

Slave traders took black people from many different cultures in Africa, and put them all together in the Caribbean – where the culture was a white-imposed one. In the 1950s, Afro-Caribbeans came to the UK when they were offered work here, and expected equal treatment with white people. The realisation that this was not the case often led to mental illness, exacerbated by not having an indigenous culture that they could call their own to fall back on. This contrasts with the experience of Asians from the Indian subcontinent.

Glover's questioning of motive in psychiatric diagnosis, and the hidden influence of our culture and the drive to conform with it, was taken up and developed in a different direction by our second speaker. Kay Redfield Jamison is a Professor of Psychiatry at Johns Hopkins University. She began: 'I am a scientist and a clinician, but I am also someone who suffers from a severe mental illness – manic depression. My remarks will reflect these different perspectives.'

She dealt with two themes. First, suicide and our failure to prevent an epidemic of self-destruction among so many (especially young) people. Second, the relationship between mental illness and creativity.

Her use of statistics shocks. Suicide in the US is 'the third major cause of death in 15–19 year olds, and it is the second leading cause of death in college students ... across the world, in those between the ages of 15 and 44, suicide is the second leading killer of women and the fourth of men'. It seems that the failure to prevent suicide reflects the stigma that attaches to mental illness in our society. I would also add, in Anglo-Saxon culture, to the expression of emotion. Jamison refers to the array of effective pyschotropic medicines and psychotherapies available to treat the underlying mental causes of suicide, and contrasts this with the failure of public health interventions. Again, we are brought face to face with the paradox of the clinical and the political tasks of medicine.

In passages that crackle with their own poetic creativity, Jamison calls in support of her association of madness and creativity, great poets, painters and thinkers. As with Glover's contribution, one senses an underlying sympathy with the mood music of the 1960s, and with R D Laing's[10] romantic notion of schizophrenia as alternative artistic, even spiritual, enlightenment – though both would, I think, sharply distance themselves from the inferences about the nature and causes of mental illness that Laing drew.

The message from both Glover and Jamison reprises the warnings given in earlier sessions when we had contemplated the future elimination of 'bad' genes: when the genetic locations of schizophrenia and manic depression have definitively been found, we should be wary of attempting to exclude these components of our humanity. The harm they inflict on a minority may be immeasurably outweighed by the potential benefits to the majority in the generation of creativity, adaptive risk-taking and social cohesion.

Living well, dying well

In October we looked at the links between the quantity of a life's span and its quality. We asked:

> *What determines the way we think about the end of life? Does living a full and healthy life include contemplating its appropriate end? Do we allow anxieties about death to spoil a good life? What do patients and doctors mean when they talk about 'risk' and 'chances'? What entitlements and responsibilities do we have for ourselves and others, in making, or denying, choices about how to die? How can we make the quality of the end of life part of the quality of living it?*

We chose as our first speaker Dr Bert Keizer, who has written much about the medical task at the end of life, and whose name is associated with the growth of euthanasia in Holland. It was, therefore, scarcely surprising that much of the evening was taken up with talk about the morality of a voluntary purposive ending of life, and the quality of life's ending.

In a lucid set of propositions from Dr Rowan Williams, Archbishop of Wales, we were offered reflections on the quality of a life and a death, and also, what seems to matter so much to the suffering patient, something about our perception of life's meaning. In this the Archbishop made clear the part played by religious belief.

There can be no doubt about the deep controversy that Bert Keizer's views can engender. On the evidence of that October evening, there could also be no doubt about the genuineness of his humane concern for his patients, or of his anger at the arrogance and stupidities of much modern medicine. His case, that we be allowed help to die as far as possible as responsible adults in some command of our lives, and deserving of respect and dignity in our dying, was made with persuasive force.

The Archbishop held that, in the Christian view of life, euthanasia was unacceptable. For Keizer, to deny the suffering patient the option of euthanasia could be inhumane. What characterised the ensuing discussion between them, the panellists and the audience, was the shared recognition that these issues are too painful and important for brassy rhetoric, and too imminent for us all to admit of evasion and fudge.

Having in the first half of his address listed modern medicine's inability to intervene curatively in so many contemporary plagues, in the second half Keizer allowed two stories to persuade us of the dangers of a biomechanical medicine, divorced from the biography of the patient. The first story was the record of Byron's death at the hands of his doctors in 1824. It was an all-too-familiar account of the best that medical expertise then had on offer: bleeding by cutting open the veins, applying leeches to the scalp, bowel purges, blistering of the skin and the like. This was a euthanasia as unintentional on the doctors' side as it was involuntary on the patient's.

Keizer then rolled the calendar forward 170 years to 1994, and described the shocking, though again unintended, torture of his own father at the hands of doctors whose belief in their high technical nostrums was no less genuine and convinced than that of Byron's doctors in theirs. And no less misplaced.

It became clear that, in Keizer's view, euthanasia was more than the option of a gentle and timely exit from a life already drawing to a suffering close. It was as importantly the means of rescuing us from the torturing consequences of modern medicine's technical extravagances at the ebbing of our lives.

The powerful seductions of medicine's technology can come dressed in strange guise. This was an illustrative story discussed subsequently by the panellists. Some months earlier, a 15-year-old girl dying from heart disease had refused to accept a heart transplant because she could not contemplate living with 'a dead person's heart' inside her. The notion was repugnant and she preferred to die of her disease. In the event she was deemed too immature to make this judgement, and persuaded to accept the treatment – which, by the way, will entail her having to take a complex regime of immunosuppresant medication for the indefinite future, with its attendant distressing side effects. In one study the commonest cause of renal transplant rejection was found to be a failure of the patient to adhere to such a difficult and unpleasant regime of medicines.[11]

Williams quotes with approval Ernest Becker's broadside: 'psychiatry, which gives us so many of the tools we need to understand our terror of death and the mechanisms of avoidance, has itself become a mechanism of avoidance.' I detect some ambivalence here. Psychiatry, and in the USA particularly the psychiatry of the Freudians and their many analogues, has often seemed to take upon itself the role of a new secular religion, with offers of insight as salvation. Yet the thesis that Williams develops seems to echo the language of the Freudians. This is scarcely surprising when one recalls that Freud's term 'psyche' has persistently been mistranslated from its German context as 'mind'. Freud used the term 'psyche' to mean 'soul'.[12] Williams says that: 'the bare fact of suffering is first and foremost a moral challenge: can this be taken into the picture I have of myself, can I make my story out of this?' The task of life becomes increasingly clear to us precisely because we are to face our death: 'as I discover that I shall die, I return to question what I hope for my life.'

These ideas stirred strong memories in me. The tasks of the general practitioner are simultaneously biographical and biomechanical. For the patient who comes to have intimations of her death, the end of life may pose a question framed in both meanings of that word: the end as finality, and the end as purpose. Her suffering does indeed present a moral challenge, but it also cries out for technical help.

I was intrigued to learn how Archbishop Williams would argue against euthanasia without reference to divine authority – which would have left this non-believer with nothing but the void of his unbelief. In fact the argument, when it came, was powerful and cogent, and if it did not totally persuade me, it certainly gave great cause for more thought.

He based his case on the view of the human as innately social: 'for all the major religious traditions, the good is achieved only by corporate action.' This social perspective sees each of us as deeply implicated in all the others – and I could not help wondering: 'Does the Archbishop really mean *all* the others?' I suspect that he really does, and it leads him to assert: 'The substantial goods of the moral world cannot be attained by summing up or adding together sets of individual achievements.' He concludes that his ground for finding euthanasia wrong is 'not even the belief that life is 'sacred', but the belief that lives are deeply implicated with each other to the extent that violence against oneself (even in extreme circumstances) has to be violence against others as well'.

The humanity of Keizer, the doctor, and Williams, the priest, shone through the debate that followed. I was left uneasy by the thought that bringing a wretched terminal illness to a purposive and accepted and peaceful end could be seen as violence to the self, and therefore to others. I doubt that it felt like that to Bert Keizer and his patients. But I was also left uneasy by the thought that my assumption, that the doctor's first response must be to relieve the suffering by whatever medicines he can employ, may reflect a mechanistic view of that suffering which rather misses the point.

Health in the city

In November, to conclude our series of debates, we came home. The teaching hospitals of Guy's and St Thomas', and Southwark Cathedral, sit on the South Bank of the Thames in south-east London. The sparkling new university buildings and towering cliffs of Guy's Hospital, architectural sculptures in glass and steel, are stunningly arresting. The majesty of the Cathedral, refurbished for the Millennium, its ancient stones scrubbed bright and golden, speaks of strong faith in a good future. The neighbourhoods show, almost cheek by jowl, the wastelands of poor public housing, and designer chic apartments in the loft conversions on the waterfront. The inner city population immediately served by our teaching hospitals and the Cathedral is multi-ethnic in origin, and poverty and wealth, good citizenship and social exclusion, live side by side in many of its streets. We looked at the impact of city life on health, and asked:

> *Is the city now an outmoded concept, to be supplanted by new configurations of domestic living, social interaction, work and recreation? What will we mean by a healthy place to live? Twenty years hence, in a changing built environment, what sort of health services will we need; where will they be located; what sorts of health care personnel and organisations will provide them?*

Our speakers developed complementary themes. Julian Le Grand, Richard Titmuss Professor of Social Policy at the London School of Economics, examined in some depth the evidence that cities were unhealthy places. In fact, as both speakers had found, the data could be interpreted in a number of ways. The health of city people was not always demonstrably worse than that of country people, though the trend in most studies suggested that it was. There was, however, another finding with profound implications for future public policy. Le Grand found that 'those in urban areas – that is, in cities – *feel* in worse health than those in rural and suburban areas, but *are* actually in better health'. This paradox sets a puzzle: 'Why are the inhabitants of cities getting better but feeling worse than their country brethren?'

Our second speaker, Victor Rodwin, Professor of Health Policy and Management at the Wagner School of Public Service at New York University, asked: 'Are cities socially infected breeding grounds for disease?' and concluded that they were. In New York, London, Paris and Tokyo there is failure to deal adequately with fresh epidemics of infectious diseases, including AIDS. There are problems with water and air pollution, homelessness, poverty, the exclusion of ethnic minority groups, and terrorism. Chillingly, he reminded us of the World Trade Center bombing in New York, and the release of sarin gas in Tokyo's subway system. All this in the context of growing socio-economic inequality. Implied is the question: 'Is this context or cause?' Implied also, and intriguingly, is the link that Rodwin makes between TB and AIDS, which can be described in terms of a biomechanical model, and urban terrorism that cannot.

The nineteenth-century German pathologist Rudolph Virchow[13] famously averred that medicine was a social science. He had been invited to investigate the causes and containment of a typhus epidemic among immigrant Polish workers in Silesia. Doubtless to the consternation of the Prussian government that had commissioned him, his recommendations were concerned not with biological control, but with ameliorating the hardships and injustices experienced by the workers. In his report he advised improving their education, increasing their income, involving them in local politics, and accepting Polish as an official language. What model of disease could possibly have linked denying the use of a mother tongue with the severity of the typhus' contagion in that group? What linked the insights of Virchow, the political radical, with those of Virchow, the medical scientist?

These yoked insights (TB and terrorism; typhus and political exclusion) echoed again in Le Grand's preferred explanation for his paradoxical findings about the health perceptions of city dwellers – that they are getting better and feeling worse. He believed that the concept of 'social capital', and its absence from the lives of most in our urban ghettos, could be the key to solving what he describes as his 'puzzle'. He quoted the description given by Robert Puttnam, the originator of the idea: 'the features of social life – networks, norms and trust – that enable participants to act together more effectively to pursue shared objectives.'

In a key passage in his address, Le Grand links a sense of well-being to social support and civic engagement, and quotes many studies whose findings support this contention. In recent years, and in similar vein, John Howie[14] and colleagues in Edinburgh, seeking to measure the quality of consultations between doctors and patients in a deprived inner city environment, evolved the concept of 'enablement'. R G Wilkinson,[15] writing in 1992 about the link between income distribution and life expectancy, commented: 'The social consequences of people's differing circumstances in terms of stress, self-esteem and social relations may now be one of the most important influences on health.' It is not the material consequences of exclusion that seems to do the damage as much as the self-awareness of it.

Our speakers were leading us toward their preferred (and largely shared) remedies. The notion of social engineering, rather like the notion of genetic engineering, may start with high ideals and end in something unrecognisably awful. But there are precedents that may allow us some optimism. Rodwin refers to a paper given in 1875 by Benjamin Ward Richardson, a disciple of Edwin Chadwick. He says that in *Hygeia: a city of health*, Richardson's vision of a city designed for health inspired Ebenezer Howard and the 'Garden City' movement of the 1890s, and perhaps, in the late 1980s, the World Health Organisation's 'Healthy Cities' movement.

Le Grand concludes that the improvement of health in the city lies in linking health with empowerment. Better health empowers people, and empowering people gives them better health. Yet again, as in all our previous debates, we returned to seek ways of curtailing the control of State and the professions in order to make room for the health, the self-actualisation, of the individual. And yet again, we were made aware, at every step, of the need to curtail the self-actualisation of the individual, in order to make room for the flowering of a healthy and co-operative society.

Boundaries

This has been a very personal reflection on a series of debates to which I could never do justice here. Our intention was to open up for public examination those aspects of medical advance and social change that will profoundly affect the lives of us all. In particular we were concerned to reach out to our own local communities, to invite its citizens to share in the debates, and to encourage them to take these further in their many social and civic encounters.

This was not an exercise that permits me to sum up. That would be not only premature but impudent. The debates will only have been successful if they remain (perhaps permanently) unfinished, and if no one appropriates to herself or himself the power definitively to decide. What will remain of importance in what we undertook, and may be of some enduring value, is not the answers that we gave, but the care with which we framed and will in future re-frame the questions.

The German Protestant theologian Paul Tillich[16] said that he had lived his life on many boundaries – between socialism and capitalism, between the Old World and the New, between art and science, between the spiritual and the materialistic – and he concluded that the boundary was the best, the most exciting, place to be. It is on boundaries (and perhaps only there) that discovery happens. In our millennial programme we stretched, as far as were able, towards the imminent boundary with our future. Sometimes, I think, we may have glimpsed the limits of what's human.

Acknowledgements

I am deeply grateful to our distinguished speakers and discussion panel members, and to the six audiences, on whose ideas I have drawn freely, and in the most biased of fashions. To Professor Sir Cyril Chantler, Dean of the Medical School throughout the period of the Festival, and the Very Reverend Colin Slee, Dean of Southwark Cathedral, I owe large debts of gratitude for their support and good friendship, and for their critiques of an early draft. They bear no responsibility for the many shortcomings of what I have written here, but they have saved the reader from far worse.

Marshall Marinker

References

1. Eliot T S. *Four quartets*. London: Faber and Faber, 1954.
2. Dyson F. *Imagined worlds*. Harvard: Harvard University Press, 1997.
3. General Medical Council. *Tomorrow's doctors*. London: GMC, 1993.
4. Hart J T. The inverse care law. *Lancet* 1971; 1: 405–12.
5. Day-Lewis C. *The room and other poems*. London: Jonathan Cape, 1965.
6. McCormick J, Anderson D. *Risk, health and the consumer*. London: The Social Affairs Unit, 1992.
7. Skrabanek P, McCormick J. *Follies and fallacies in medicine*. Whithorn: Tarragon Press, 1998.
8. Jenkins R, Smeeton N, Marinker M, Shepherd M. Study of the classification of mental illness in general practice. *Psychol Med* 1985; 15: 403–09
9. Foucault M. *The birth of the clinic*. London: Tavistock Press, 1963.
10. Laing R D. *The voice of experience*. London: Allen Lane, 1982.
11. Rovelli M, Palmeri D, Vossler E, Bartus S, Hull D, Schweizer R. Non-compliance in organ transplant recipients. *Transplantation Proceedings* 1989; 21 (1): 833–34.
12. Bettelheim B. *Freud and man's soul*. London: Chatto and Windus, 1982.
13. See Rosen R G. *From medical police to social medicine*. New York: Yale University Press, 1974.
14. Howie J, Heaney D, Maxwell M, Walker J. A comparison of a Patient Enablement Instrument (PEI) against two established satisfaction scales as an outcome measure of primary care consultations. *Family Practice* 1998; 15 (1): 165–71.
15. Wilkinson R G. Income distribution and life expectancy. *BMJ* 1992; 304: 165–68.
16. Tillich P. *On the boundary*. London: Collins, 1967.

Chapter 2

Health and justice (1)

Kenneth Minogue

'Health' and 'justice' name perhaps the two most desirable of all human perfections. My grandmother used to say: 'As long as you've got your health ...' in her more Panglossian moments, and the philosopher John Rawls begins his treatise on justice by telling us that 'Justice is the first virtue of social institutions, as truth is of systems of thought.'

I am, however, a sceptic, and I propose to treat both ideas a little roughly. In particular, we must begin by recognising that the idea of justice is highly contestable. It has two quite distinct meanings:

(a) The structure of abstract rules – the rule of law – within which people are able to live in a decent society. Such rules depend for effectiveness on enforcement by authority.

(b) A specific condition of things, an end-state – often these days called 'social justice' – that we ought to bring about, and incorporating, for example, some desirable distribution of goods, including health.

These are not merely distinct meanings of justice. They directly contradict each other, because no set of abstract rules can, given free human decisions, generate the desirable condition. A liberal and a perfect society are incompatible ideals.

Health and justice might be related in a variety of ways, but for our purposes they seem to point to an issue conceived in terms of one statistical fact: namely, that the poor, on average, die at a younger age than the rich. It may also be that they suffer more illness. In terms of medical need, then, they ought to receive more medical care and attention. But where individuals must pay for health care from their own resources, the poor, having fewer resources, will get less of it, while the rich, who need less of it, will have more. This is the basis of Dr Hart's 'inverse care law', which affirms, I think, that those who get the most care need it least, and those who need it most get less of it.

In these considerations lies the basic syllogism whose conclusion became the National Health Service. But that institution is now under criticism on many fronts.

In discussing health and justice, our first move must be away from the abstractions and towards their custodians. The custodians of justice are politicians, judges and lawyers; those of health are doctors and nurses. Both groups are a bit like motor mechanics, in that they come into play only when something goes wrong. Mechanics don't actually make the motor cars, and similarly doctors don't 'cause' health. They merely remove some impediments to it, and permit nature to take its course.

Another reason why this is important is that abstractions have no interests of their own, but judges and doctors are, for some purposes, corporate bodies with interests of their own, which may at times be in conflict with those of the people they serve.

Let us now explore a little the phenomenology of medical experience. It begins in the doctor–patient relationship. In principle, the doctor serves the patient's interest in being restored to health. This relationship is at the heart of much medical thinking. Illness and diagnosis can take a variety of forms, and Professor Marinker has analysed a variety of ways of construing this situation: the patient as diagnosis (that the patient and not the disease is the object of inquiry); the family as illness (in which the inquiry spreads beyond the individual to the group); the illness as risk (the concern with possible future developments in terms of risk factors); and illness as commodity (in which cost-benefit factors appear when considering the problem). These are interesting categories, but for reasons that will appear, I think it interesting that medical reflection does not seem to regard as important the intelligence and capacity for self-help in the conduct of the patients themselves.

Now doctors will often find themselves tidying up the mess left by other activities. The casualty surgeon in warfare, for example, charged with taking the bullets out of soldiers who have been shot by other soldiers, could hardly help thinking that the real solution here might well be a pacific or pacified world. Again, the doctor charged with curing the dyspepsia of an out-of-condition gourmet might well say: 'I cannot do much for you. The only serious care for your affliction is that you should change your way of life. Eat less, exercise more, my dear fellow, and you will be altogether better.'

Let us call this impulse to transcend medical problems by changing society 'perfectionism'. It arises from a taste for ultimate solutions. It resembles what political scientists call 'utopianism', but it seems to me better not to have an evidently political term for what I am considering. In a similar way, the judge might conclude from the fact that many of the criminals who have come before him are poor and uneducated that the problem lies in the system of society rather than the system of justice. For doctors, the epidemiological temptation consists in abandoning pills and the stethoscope in favour of the rostrum.

The proposition I wish to advance is that perfectionism entails collectivism. It means that doctors follow the Platonic path of telling us how we ought to live. The key concept of perfectionism is the thing called a 'social problem'. Let us analyse it.

A problem is anything that we construe as an impediment to happiness or as a cause of pain, and we live in a civilisation in which the distinction between the things we can change and things we must endure has virtually disappeared. Anything we don't like becomes a problem, and we search for things to do about it. What has not changed, however, is the enormous and contradictory variety of ways in which human beings respond to the world and the different ways in which they find their happiness. We standardly regard illness as a problem, but we should not forget that there are cases in which it serves as a solution to intricate personal situations. Masochists enjoy pain, and hypochondriacs have an ambiguous relationship with it. Hence the key word in that sentence was 'standardly'. In order to operate in this collectivised construction of the world, we must homogenise the human condition.

So much for 'problem'. The word 'social' simply means, if it means anything, that we are dealing with more than one individual. And this move of interpretation is an invitation for governments to appear with a strategy for solving the social problem.

This is, of course, conceptually tricky country, and my observation about the variety of human responses might be countered by taking masochists and hypochondriacs and people looking for a disability certificate as people who lack 'health' in some wider sense of the term. Perfectionism thus dangles before us the possibility of a single world populated by entirely healthy and happy human beings who are no longer seduced by the distortions of their social situation into a variety of morbid responses. Perfectionism, in other words, presumes perfectibility.

It is this manner of thinking that brings together our two abstractions of health and justice. The argument runs, in one of its forms:

> *Because society is unjustly organised into rich and poor having disparate resources for health, some people suffer from more ill health than others, and this variation is an 'injustice' whose cause lies entirely in the structure of our society.*

Since this is a social problem, the solution lies in the State creating a system that provides health care without reference to the patient's 'ability' to pay. And two assumptions here seem to me important. The first is that health is something that can be provided for a (passive) individual; the second is that the only issue is something abstractly described as the 'ability' to pay, rather than, for example, also raising questions about the priorities of the individual concerned.

The distinction we need to make, then, is between individualist and collectivist responses to the problems of ill health. Medicine inherits the individualist relationship between doctor and patient, while collectivism seeks a much more ambitious field of operations. And the essential point is that collectivism is not just individualism writ large. It is a different kind of relationship altogether, and for a number of reasons:

(a) Individualism requires the doctor to give advice in terms of the actual beliefs and desires of the patient himself or herself; collectivism involves the patient being treated in terms of some overarching priority, which, as the State gets involved, becomes some national priority.

(b) The individualist relationship is between two self-conscious persons intelligently responding to their situation; the logic involved is hypothetical, in which the requirements of the individual constitute the antecedents of inquiry. Collectivism involves the causal logic of technology; the public health officer is concerned to change a variety of social indicators, such as a teenage suicide rate or a level of obesity.

(c) Individualism operates within the laws of society; collectivism has been incorporated within some extended sense of justice, in which the laws themselves may be used as instruments of alleged medical desirability, as in legislation discouraging smoking. The State itself can determine the outcome.

(d) George Bernard Shaw observed that the professions were a conspiracy against the public interest, and the doctor–patient relationship certainly has its hazards. Some doctors may well specialise in what Tom Lehrer once cynically called 'diseases of the rich' and dentists have been known to fill an idle hour with unneeded dental work. On the other hand, in collectivism the patient is subjected to the demands of public interest, with all the ambiguities of that term. Individual choice has little to do with it.

(e) Collective medicine prescribes in ignorance of the patient's individual needs, while in the doctor–patient relationship those needs are in principle paramount.

(f) In the doctor–patient relationship, the doctor need not pretend to know more than he actually does, and any deceptions (such as the use of a placebo) are based on some sort of direct knowledge. The public health expert, however, is forced to declare what is currently taken to be knowledge as if it were the ultimate truth. Worse, he is constrained to assume the stupidity of his charges, as for example in recommendations about the benefits or dangers of different forms of alcohol. Patients as a class must be 'educated' to have the right attitude to solving the abstract form of whatever the problem might be. The public health officer operates in terms of managerial criteria such as performance indicators, and in the background of his judgement lies the political and economic calculations in terms of which the system is managed. It is not unknown for these to run counter to the best interests of individuals.

In the collectivist system, the patient inevitably becomes more abstract, and this has important consequences. The relationship between doctor and patient is a moral relationship, involving responsibility on one side and gratitude on the other. The relationship between the public health officer and his population is a political one. No one feels gratitude to the Surgeon General; gratitude has no place in the relationship. Here the appropriate activity of the patients is to agitate for better conditions. Discussion is about better performance in securing the implementation of the 'right' to medical care free at the point of need. And in case these considerations should seem to be unbearably abstract, let me simply mention the growing problem of irresponsible call outs of doctors (under the unlamented Citizens' Charter) and the violence met by doctors and nurses today as they go about their tasks.

It is an important fact that in a moral relationship individuals reveal themselves in terms of their virtues and vices – courage, prudence, intelligence, fussiness, fear and so on. This is not at all the same as abstract individuals conceived in terms of needs.

The general problem of health and justice thus points us towards an important problem in modern societies. We might put it this way: in virtually all previous societies, some element of hierarchy means that those less capable are looked after by those more capable. This is often the way extended families have worked, and the feudal system was a hierarchy of nobles at the top and clients at the bottom. Our own society operates on the counter-factual assumption that all its members are capable of managing their own lives. For a great variety of reasons, this is not true. Anything from physical disability to drug addiction can make a whole class of people incapable of looking after themselves. We might thus set up, very much against the grain of current thinking, a distinction between the competent and the incompetent members of society.

The competent are, of course, the vast majority, and they are the ones who can usefully enter into the doctor–patient relationship. The incompetent are those who cannot manage – sometimes merely as the result of some temporary problem, sometimes because of a lifelong condition. This distinction is not at all to be identified with that between rich and poor, though it intersects with it.

The problem, then, is one of public policy, and on the view I am presenting there is no need at all for a public policy relating to the competent, except perhaps at the margins involving highly expensive operations. On the other hand, we are all agreed that everyone ought to have access to medical care when needed. In earlier times – times when access to a doctor was much more limited, and when indeed doctors were quite likely to do as much harm as good – this distinction operated, with the competent making their own arrangements, and 'the poor' being served, if served at all, by charitable institutions. The NHS has reversed this balance, with most people being cared for by the NHS and a few buying medical care.

The argument is often floated that if everyone were forced to use the one national service, its standards would be improved. Analogous arguments demand the abolition of private education.

My argument, however, is that collectivist medicine, although it has a place in modern life, corrupts both the patient – who becomes a mere agitator for better services at no apparent cost to himself – and the doctor – who loses his professional identity and becomes a State official significantly moved by bureaucratic considerations.

There is no doubt that health problems, if understood as social problems, are intractable. They seems to me to be made even more intractable by our current insistence that all patients are the same, and by our failure to recognise the difference between those patients who merely need advice, and those whose lives must, in some degree, be managed for them.

Chapter 3

Health and justice (2)

Julian Tudor Hart

In a profit-driven society, where can justice grow?

For an opportunity occurring only once in a thousand years, one should be grateful.
I am, chiefly to my old friend and sparring partner, Marshall Marinker. At 72, I'm less
interested in the speed of social change than in its direction. Since 1979, society has
bowled forward on an accelerating casual cycle: things get bigger and better, by
making people smaller and worse.

Karl Marx and Adam Smith shared important common ground. They agreed that
human societies necessarily began as associations between co-operating equals.
Within these groups of subsistence producers, inequalities were biological rather than
social. Such communities had robust ideas of justice within societies (though often
not between societies). Such justice was normally maintained by culture,
exceptionally by expulsion to the wilderness. What Engels described in 1884, in his
now neglected *Origin of the family, private property and the state*,[1] has been almost
entirely confirmed by observation of presently surviving stone-age societies.

Marx and Smith agreed that advance beyond egalitarian subsistence depended on
divisions of labour and property, which necessarily created socially constructed
inequalities. The collective social product was no longer socially planned or
consumed. Productivity rose at the expense of social division.

There have been many attempts to justify these social inequalities biologically, first
by theories of moral selection, later by Social Darwinism and mismeasures of
intelligence.[2] Adam Smith was too great a man to deceive himself: 'Till there be
property', he wrote, 'there can be no government, the very end of which is to secure
wealth, and to defend the rich from the poor.'[3] Social Darwinism is part of that
defence, with a particular appeal to people at the top of the heap. An old friend of
mine, with lifetime experience of general practice and an international reputation in
research, is honestly convinced that the real distinction between rich and poor lies
not in their wealth or power, but their different capacities to cope with life.[4]
He seems to see that quality that so impressed F Scott Fitzgerald. Talking with
Dashiel Hammett, he said: 'Y'know, Dash, the rich are different from us.' 'Yes',

Hammett replied, 'They have more money.' My experience, or my interpretation of my experience, was entirely different from that of my GP friend. Measuring the coping power of poor people against what I thought I could have managed myself, with the same history in the same circumstances, they rarely failed to amaze me.

A much more important justification, because it has a far broader appeal, is the claim that rising inequality was, is, and will always remain, a reasonable price to pay for the colossal rise in productivity that market competition for profit alone can produce. For production of material commodities, this has so far proved true. Even if capitalism produced 3000 pairs of shoes for Imelda Marcos but left thousands of Filipino children unshod, childhood shoelessness has been virtually eliminated in all developed market economies. Even so, production for the market always and inevitably subordinates satisfaction of human needs and long-term sustainability, to profit and capital accumulation. This includes its most nonsensical feature, the deliberate invention and promotion of often illusory wants for people who already have far more commodities than they need, but still have enough wealth to support further extensions of luxury markets. The market exalts our guts and despises our brains. There has to be some better way than this.

Inequality, and thus injustice, are necessarily created by all societies in which a few live from what they own or control, leaving everyone else to depend on these owners for employment. This has been the structure of virtually all developed societies we have so far experienced. Some developing societies have tried to break out of this pattern. They used the collapse of more or less feudal or colonial economies as opportunities to create socialist societies alternative to capitalism, rather than sequels to it. The hopes they raised were intoxicating, but they've all ended as some version of industrial capitalism. Their experience proved not that Marx was wrong, but that he was right. Revolutionary leaders in a society close to collapse are necessary but not sufficient preconditions for a fundamental, permanent and sustainable shift to a sharing rather than acquisitive society, which might restore the social unity of subsistence production on a new basis of industrialised abundance. A new society needs new social institutions, new modes of production, new customs and a new common sense. These can probably be developed only within an advanced, fully industrialised economy.

Limits to charity

A hitherto essential link between social inequality and rising productivity has always been recognised. A central task of the main religions has been to explain this paradox by accounts of lost innocence and original sin, attenuate it through charity in the life we have, and evade it by letting God redress the wrongs of this world in a hypothetical world after death. In the world we actually have, charity inevitably has lower priority than profit. As Margaret Thatcher said, the Samaritan had first to get rich and stay rich before he could help anyone but himself.

Until 1979 the NHS functioned as a State charity. It was an institution for the people but not of them. Its funding depended on wealth generated from commodity production, transferred through taxation. Anyone may at any time fall among thieves, of their health and happiness as well as their property. Premature death, disability and unhappiness are socially selective. They grant their miseries most generously to the poor,[5,6] but they don't altogether forget the rich. Experience shows that if enough poor people live miserably, there are bad consequences for their betters.[7] My mother was crippled by a severe stroke at the age of 52, at the height of a well-paid career in the pharmaceutical industry. This was a consequence of childhood rheumatic heart disease, now virtually unknown in the UK, but common in slum-ridden Britain in 1916. Young doctors wanting to study acute rheumatic fever today must go to West Africa, South America or India – or to the ghettos of Chicago and New York.[8] In the UK we have not yet created new slums large enough to re-create endemic rheumatic fever, but we're sliding towards the same social model.

So, can we and should we try to create just institutions within an unjust society? The standard answer seems to be: 'Yes, but don't try too hard.' So long as the NHS is seen as a State charity – a wealth-consuming rather than wealth-producing system supporting an unfortunate sick minority by taxes levied on a fortunate healthy majority – limits to how hard we try will be set by consent to income tax and corporation tax. This can be measured in three ways.

First, news media editors get all the news about society, so they can tell us what everyone else thinks, and thus set the agenda for our own thinking. All our mass circulation newspaper companies are owned by people rich enough to buy them, and media commentators are highly paid celebrities. Try though they may, they can never see things as they appear from below. However, papers must be sold and programmes must be watched. This sets limits to how far what they publish can differ from what their readers personally experience. As most people do experience the NHS personally, the media pay at least some regard to the truth.

Second, we have rigorous scientific studies of public opinion, for example the series on British Social Attitudes conducted annually since the early 1980s by Social and Community Planning Research (SCPR).[9] These have consistently shown a large majority of people in favour of an NHS providing the entire range of effective care free for the whole population, funded from taxation. Despite all doubts thrown at this by Thatcher's New Conservatives and by the postmodern thinkers of the unthinkable, this majority has continued to grow. Despite powerful advocates for continued piecemeal and generally covert privatisation of the NHS,[10] it's probably still growing. Defence of the NHS unites voters of all persuasions. The majority in favour of a universal service provided free according to need is larger among Labour and Liberal Democrat voters, but it exists even among Conservatives. This cultural commitment to a free and universal NHS is not unique in Britain, but seems stronger and deeper here than anywhere else in Europe, possibly excepting Italy. It's certainly much greater here than in the USA.[11]

Third, we've evidence from parliamentary elections. These, we're told, are the only valid measure of what people actually believe. When they say that a richer nation must be able to afford an expanding and more generous NHS, and that even if society as a whole becomes increasingly unequal, they want a sector of our economy to work for human needs rather than profit, we're told this is meaningless: for opinion polls, people vote with their consciences, but at real elections they vote with their wallets. The 1992 election is apparently supposed to prove for all time that no party proposing higher graduated income tax for the rich can ever again get elected. According to *The Economist*, Rupert Murdoch's main UK holding company, Newscorp Investments, has paid no net corporation tax for the past 11 years, despite profits of £1.4bn over that period. Its expected tax liability of £350m could have built seven hospitals.[12] Convergence of all major parties toward a common agenda of totally business-orientated economy and culture has created a huge but inevitably transient gap in serious British politics – not the politicking of personal careers, but the real politics of choosing what sort of society we want our children and grandchildren to live in.

Once freed from fear of any socialised alternative, there are no limits to neoliberal economic thinking. Professor Milton Friedman is a Nobel Prize-winning economist who must be taken seriously. 'Few trends', he wrote, 'could so thoroughly undermine the very foundations of our free society as the acceptance by corporate officials of a social responsibility other than to make as much money for their shareholders as possible.'[13] Few other economists now seem to agree with him, but this is how the capitalist system compels corporate leaders to behave, simply to survive in dog-eat-dog international markets.

Capitalism cannot, from its own intellectual resources, set limits to greed, because subordination of human judgement to market forces is its mechanism, and greed is its fuel. To defend and extend human dimensions in a dehumanising society, we have to find forces outside the market paradigm, a credible alternative base for a fundamentally different economy, providing secure foundations for a rehumanising culture, and a higher form of common sense. In the rest of this lecture I hope to explain what this alternative might be.

The NHS is a wealth-producing industry

The NHS functions within a society geared to pursuit of profit as its aim, with satisfaction of human needs as its subordinate by-product. The key to advance lies in recognising that the NHS produces wealth in an entirely different way. Its outputs are just as real as the products of commodity production for profit, with far more scope for sustainable expansion. These outputs are measurable, but not in units interchangeable with those used for the commodity market, because they are personal and social, but not exchangeable.

During the 1980s, business attitudes and methods were imposed on the NHS. These were much influenced by health economists, notably Alain Enthoven.[14,15] By applying business attitudes and methods to the NHS, they promised large gains in productivity. In general, they failed.[16] Medical science, basic and applied, has continued to advance despite, rather than because of, business attitudes and methods. Business culture did immense damage to the morale of staff, patients, and independent university research,[17,18] reinforced by a general retreat from reason throughout society.[19] Consumer rather than supplicant status has in some ways been an advance for patients, a liberation from unaccountable professionals, but it is also a social retreat. New Labour's leaders have adopted medical consumerism, just as they have adopted competitive education. Provider–consumer relationships in the market are essentially adversarial. Optimal development of patients as co-producers of a healthy society, or of students as co-producers of an educated society, both depend on developing new co-operative, socialised relationships. Evidence from both medical and educational science consistently supports this path of development. Equally consistently, it is thwarted by market competition.

Medical science is applied science of human life – the whole of life, from cloned cells in experimental tissue culture to the lives of real people in society, in the ordinary chaos of their human activity. Doctors, nurses, and all other health workers are, whether or not they recognise and accept this role, ambassadors of science to the people; and the people, whether or not they recognise and accept this role, are users of this science. Scientific knowledge needs human intelligence to create it truthfully, and human judgement to apply it safely and efficiently. All staff, all patients, and all potential patients, are or soon will be involved in some way in creating new knowledge, and they are already involved in its application.

To say 'human intelligence' implies that there is some other sort of intelligence. Indeed there is – the intelligence of the market. The market reflects only one component of collective human behaviour, of only one part of humanity. It draws its data from people who buy, defined by the money they have in their pockets. This is a systematically skewed sample, providing a dehumanised view of humanity. It's an impoverished source of data, leading to promotion of foods to the overfed while others starve, to promotion of two cars to people who already have one while public transport falls apart, and an endless list of other examples. The market is stupid. Market-driven health care in the United States ensures not only that rich people are more profitable than poor people, but also that healthy people are more profitable than sick people. So health maintenance organisations run by giant insurance companies systematically recruit patients least likely to need help, offload patients with the biggest problems,[20,21] and take 15–20 per cent of turnover for profit.[22]

The NHS is a wealth-producing industry. Its product is health gain – healthier births, healthier lives and healthier deaths (death being always inevitable, but not necessarily unhealthy). This product is both an extremely personal gain and a social gain. It makes life better and easier for patients, while also relieving potential burdens on everyone else. And properly organised, it can help to produce new knowledge and new skills, so that the more the NHS applies medical knowledge, the more new knowledge it creates. If health care were a commodity, this exponential rise would present no problems for government. If a new, costly, but effective treatment becomes available in the commodity market, people who can be helped will buy it, the commodity economy will expand, and so will general prosperity. But alas, the NHS is a nationalised, non-profit industry, where we do things not because they're profitable, but because they're needed. In the NHS, every advance in medical science therefore presents new problems for governments claiming to act for society as a whole, but acting in practice for those with wealth and power.

The answer is to recognise the NHS as a potentially independent economy and culture, operating within its own entirely new paradigm, with its staff and the populations it serves as its political army. As the NHS emerges from its paternalist, charity-ridden past, owned by the people *de jure* but by professional establishments *de facto*, this independent economy and culture will begin to understand itself, to organise itself for political action, and to find allies in other parts of the public service economy, as well as its original supporters among workers in commodity production. Paternalism is crumbling, attacked by government, continuing the anti-professional, consumerist agenda initiated by Margaret Thatcher; by the voting public, still finding its way out of deference; and by medical science, continuing to extend research into objective studies of the processes of care, destroying delusions of grandeur long typical of health care professionals, and replacing this by justified pride in useful work shared with their patients.

Clinical judgements as economic activity

Studies of how optimal clinical judgements are actually made confirm a view first advanced by Margaret Stacey in 1976,[23] which I developed further in 1992,[24] that patients can be more usefully understood, and more effectively developed, as co-producers than as consumers. Together with their professional and other carers, they are joint producers of a product measurable as health gain. This measurement is difficult, not because the gain is not real, but because its nature as a use-value can't be measured in the same way as commodity values. Health gain through care is produced as both personal and social value, but not as a commodity for sale on the market. For this fundamental reason units of output measurement such as QALYs[25] or DALYs[26] are useful for ranking the comparative efficiency of different interventions, but can't provide a cash-equivalent currency to reconcile the NHS economy with surrounding commodity production. The NHS, and the knowledge it generates, produces not aids to life or decorations for it, but expansions and extensions of life itself. This can't be expressed efficiently in the same terms as goods and services. It's a more advanced category of thought and practice.

If efficient production of health gain depends on developing patients toward co-producer roles, this has theoretical implications for health economics and practical implications for NHS policy. For the past 20 years at least, virtually all argument about NHS policy has centred on efficiency. If NHS outputs are measured with tasks performed as numerators and resources consumed (mainly staff time) as denominators, we inevitably end up with more uteruses or gall bladders removed, more coronary arteries bypassed, or more hip joints replaced, by fewer health workers in less time. And so, in the name of efficiency, we get fewer people and less time for reaching intelligent decisions jointly with intelligent patients, not only at times of referral for these procedures, but over lifetimes preceding them. The commodity approach to NHS care naturally adopted by policy-makers using business as their ultimate model is not just inappropriate, it's destructive. It reduces the space and time within which staff and patients can develop shared responsibilities through continuing anticipatory care, and pushes the NHS further towards body repairs and crisis salvage, while making continuing anticipatory care and prevention more difficult and fragmented.

Those who have kept faith with the hopes of 1945 believe we can at least start to build justice within an unjust economy, precisely by developing the new forms of economy we can create in community-based health care, schools and universities.

By doing so independently from the commodity culture of business and consumerism, we can develop a rehumanising culture, and renew hopes of a just society. The NHS provides our most important, least vulnerable material base, a sacred area for social development. To deride this as a sacred cow has always come naturally to those who milk it to their own advantage, but the majority has never been fooled. Since 1948, most people in Britain have learned to treat health care as a mutual gift, not a commodity.[27] In this area if no other, we have retained social solidarity. It's not hard to see huge, simple evils, long overdue to put right. Through acting to overcome these – and only by acting, not just by talking – we can develop the new economy, the new culture, and the new common sense of future participative democracy.

Writing of Oliver Cromwell, C H George asked: 'What more is possible in life than defiance of known evil and the courage to create and fight for new illusions?'[28] No truth is final, but as knowledge grows, less of it will prove illusory. I think we must settle for that.

References

1. Engels F. *Origin of the family, private property and the state.* London: Lawrence & Wishart, 1940.
2. Gould S J. *The mismeasure of man.* New York: W W Norton, 1981.
3. Smith A. *An enquiry into the nature and causes of the wealth of nations.* Oxford: Oxford University Press, 1984 (originally published 1762).
4. Crombie D L. *Social class and health status: inequality or difference?* RCGP occasional paper 25. London: RCGP, 1984.
5. Saxena S, Majeed A, Jones M. Socioeconomic differences in childhood consultation rates in general practice in England and Wales: prospective cohort study. *BMJ* 1999; 318: 642–46.
6. Eachus J, Williams M, Chan P, Smith G D, Grainge M, Donovan J, Frankel S. Deprivation and cause specific morbidity: evidence from Somerset and Avon survey of health. *BMJ* 1996; 312: 287–92.
7. Wallace R, Wallace D. Socioeconomic determinants of health: community marginalisation and the diffusion of disease and disorder in the United States. *BMJ* 1997; 314: 1341–45.
8. McCord C, Freeman H P. Excess mortality in Harlem. *New England Journal of Medicine* 1990; 322: 173–77.
9. Jowell R, Curtis J, Park A, Brook L, Thompson K, Bryson C, editors. *British social attitudes: the 14th report: the end of Conservative values?* Aldershot: Ashgate Publishing/SCPR, 1997.
10. Bosanquet N, Polland S. *Ready for treatment: popular expectations and the future of health care.* London: Social Market Foundation, 1997.
11. Jowell R, Witherspoon S, Brook L. *British social attitudes: special international report.* Aldershot: SCPR & Gower Publishing, 1989.
12. *The Economist* 1999; 20 March.
13. Friedman M, Friedman R D. *Capitalism and freedom.* Chicago: University of Chicago Press, 1962.
14. Enthoven A. *Reflections on the management of the National Health Service: an American looks at incentives to efficiency in health services management in the UK.* Occasional papers no. 5. London: Nuffield Provincial Hospitals Trust, 1985.
15. Waitzkin H. The strange career of managed competition: military failure to medical success? *Journal of the American Public Health Association* 1994; 84: 482–89.
16. Enthoven A C. Why managed health care has failed to contain health costs. *Health Affairs* 1993; 12: 27–43.
17. Lee-Potter J. *A damn bad business: the NHS deformed.* London: Victor Gollancz, 1997.
18. Wolinsky H. Ethics in managed care. *Lancet* 1995; 346: 1499.
19. Gillot J, Kumar M. *Science and the retreat from reason.* London: Merlin Press, 1993.
20. Glasser R J. The doctor is not in: on the managed failure of managed medical care. *Harper's Magazine* 1998: March: 35–41.
21. Kassirer J P. The new health care game. *New England Journal of Medicine* 1996; 335: 443.
22. Reinhardt U E. Comment on the Jackson Hole Initiative for a twenty first century American health care system. *Health Economics* 1993; 2: 7–14.

23. Stacet N. The health service consumer: a sociological misconception. In: Stacey M, editor. *The sociology of the National Health Service*. Sociological Review Monograph 22. Keele University, 1996: 194–200.

24. Hart J T. Two paths for medical practice. *Lancet* 1992; 340: 722–25.

25. Rosser R H. From health indicators to quality adjusted life years: technical and ethical issues. In: Hopkins A, Costain D, editors. *Measuring the outcomes of medical care*. London: Royal College of Physicians of London, 1999: 1–16.

26. Arneson T, Nord E. The value of DALY life: problems with ethics and validity of disability adjusted life years. *BMJ* 1999; 319: 1423–25.

27. Titmuss R M, Oakley A, Ashton J, editors. *The gift relationship: from human blood to social policy*. Original edition with new chapters by Virginia Berridge, Vanessa Martlew, Gillian Weaver, Susan Williams and Julian Le Grand. London: London School of Economics and Political Science, 1997: 15–40.

28. George C H. *Revolution*. New York, 1962: 319.

Lord Winston gave an extempore address and felt unable to provide us with a written and edited version of his address. Consequently, we reproduce here the transcript taken from the recording made at the time.

Chapter 4

Staying human (1)

Robert Winston

Let's go back to the island of Kos, shall we, and one of the things that Hippocrates did, really, was to allow people to heal without intervention. He used the strength of the human body, and I think as Professor Chantler has pointed out, what we are now doing is interfering in a way that was never hitherto possible, and perhaps our technology is still most effective when it actually enhances the capability of the body to heal itself. And in some respects, I suppose, that's what I'm going to talk about.

What I'm going to do this evening is to really comb down on my own field – to use that as a kind of model for so much of what is relevant about staying human – and I'm going to take the notion of staying human quite literally, because I want to explore with you what seems to be, at one level, a completely fantastic view of the way at least my branch of medicine is going, and possibly much of genetics may go, not in the near future, but in the long-term future. Because I think it's a kind of appropriate thing to be talking about, particularly as we have the privilege of hearing what Bishop Harries will have to say about the dimension of this for humanity and for our view of ourselves.

My own field really threatens two core areas that we are concerned with: one, of course, is our notion of the family. It's worth bearing in mind that William Farr, who I think was the first registrar in the Office of Population and Census Studies back in around about 1832, drew up what were remarkably effective statistics of England and Wales. And he showed that in the 1830s, roughly 4 per cent of the population were illegitimate. By 1900 it was still around about 4 per cent of the population that were born out of wedlock, and that remained true until the First World War, when the figure staggeringly rose to around 6 per cent, at about the mid-term of the war. And it fell again, after the First World War, to 4 per cent, and remained like that, until 1940, when it rose again to about 5 per cent during the Second World War, and it fell again to around 4 per cent, and it stayed like that.

In the last 10, 15, 20 years, we've seen a dramatic shift; the fact is that now, at the present time, something like 40 per cent of children born in the United Kingdom are born out of wedlock. So it's not just the sort of technology that reproductive physicians like me do, which apparently seem to threaten the family. Now, my own view is that the family actually is not threatened at all by these statistics. My own view is that we have to look at them in a much more general context. We are the product, in my view, of hundreds of thousands of years of evolution; and it seems to me that you do not change human nature in a few decades, a few centuries, a few millennia. I think that just as our ancestors in their start in Africa had anger, had love, had compassion, had those human emotions, had feelings for their family; we still have those emotions, and I think we will continue to have them. And therefore I think the vista of the brave new world painted by Aldous Huxley – the notion that we will be able to engineer people outside the womb – is alive for two reasons: actually, firstly because I think it's probably biologically impossible, but more importantly, because I think fundamentally, women will want to continue to bear their children – they will want to have the experience, and indeed the pain, of childbirth. And so I have at the back of my whole philosophy about this subject, huge confidence in human nature, and I have to state that as a biased view at the start.

The second reason why I think our technology, our reproductive technology particularly, is of concern, is because it doesn't only threaten the family, but it appears to threaten our humanity, and I'll come back to that in a second. But it's as possible that genetic engineering, for example 'Dolly the sheep' or whatever, may actually, if implemented, in some way, completely change the way we are, the way we think about ourselves, the way we relate to each other as humans.

Now there are four areas that I want to briefly put in front of you during this short introduction to this debate. It seems to me almost certain that within the next five, maybe ten years, it will be possible to select the sex of your child. It's never been possible before, although there is no doubt that for ages humans have tried to sex select. There are records from certainly Ancient Greece, there are very good records in the Talmud, round about the fifth century, that have recipes suggesting how you might sex select. Interestingly, no moral dimension was placed on those early things; it wasn't regarded as being a good thing or a bad thing to be able to select the sex of your child, and of course in recent times all sorts of people have written hair-brained, pseudo-medical recipes for doing that. But until the last ten years it's not been possible at all, and it was started, really, with the ability for us to select human embryos during *in vitro* fertilisations; it's possible to fertilise a human egg, take a cell away from that egg, analyse the DNA, and see whether or not there is a male or a female chromosome present, and then transfer an embryo back to the uterus.

That's been possible for ten years; the first baby born as a result of this technology will actually be ten years old next month. However, the procedure's so complicated that it's not practically useful, except for a very small group of people, for whom it was intended. It was intended for those families who have lost a child, or who are likely to lose a child through a sex-link disorder. There are, ladies and gentlemen, about 300 or so diseases, the commonest of which is haemophilia, a blood clotting disorder, which of course affected the Russian royal family. There are about 300 of these disorders, which affect primarily males, not exclusively males, but nearly always males, but are carried by the female. And it seemed to us working in the field that it was better, morally, for these patients to try to start a pregnancy from the beginning, knowing it was free from the defect, than to go through the agonising decision that they might be faced with of watching a child die, which I think is a moral difficulty, or of course considering the legal possibility, leaving aside the moral issue, of terminating the child once it was formed inside the uterus. And so this form of sex selection was set up for that purpose.

But as I say, within the next five or ten years, there are going to be techniques that enable us to sperm-separate. Using molecular technology it will be possible, I think, to choose the sex of your child probably a great deal more easily, and then I think there are real issues that are raised by this, not least of which are the value that we place on our children – the notion that we might cause unequal distribution of males and females in our society, and the other things that develop. My own view is that is quite capable of being coped with by society, but it raises a major issue about our relationship to ourselves.

The second issue I want to raise is the notion of genetic selection. Now, with the rise in knowledge of our genetics, we can, with a fair degree of certainty, predict whether certain individuals will end up with a specific gene disorder, which may be very, very serious, or more probably fatal. There are, as it happens, about 5000 or so disorders that are fatal or if not fatal, very serious, and some of which can be detected by analysis of the DNA, using the embryonic approach that I described to you after *in vitro* fertilisation. And this is, I think, a real issue for current discussion. The view that I take about this is that it seems to me to be morally acceptable for those people who want it; it seems to me that we are given God-given tools of knowledge that we should be using if we can, and perhaps not to pursue that knowledge is not something which is morally justified.

But, of course, in leading to that notion of choosing an embryo, raises that possibility that we might treat children as a commodity, that we might have expectations of our children which they end up not fulfilling, and that, in turn, those children are thus rejected by the parents who have chosen those sorts of attributes. It certainly might apply to sex, and it might even apply to gene disorders.

But above all, and finally, my last two points, it might, of course, be a particular concern with the next stage, I think, of where we are turning. Over the last 20 years, it's been possible, in animals, very, very valuably, to create transgenic models – it's possible to inject a gene into a mouse embryo, and then to study the effects of that injected gene in the offspring that are produced as a result of that experiment. I would maintain that transgenic technology has been, as it turns out, genetic modification, but in animals, has been one of the most, if not the most, single valuable advance made in the history, in recent years, of medicine. It is extremely important because it tells us how genes work, it tells us what happens, sometimes, when a gene is missing, and it gives us all sorts of information about the fundamental basis for human disease, because the basis for human disease is very largely genetic.

But this technology, which at the moment is very inefficient, cannot be applied to humans. But it might be. It can't be applied at the moment to humans because it is, frankly, unpredictable; in the mouse, if you inject a gene into an embryo, you probably have a 2 per cent or 3 per cent chance that the mouse you produce actually ends up having the gene and expressing the part of the gene you want. Most of the time nothing happens, or the embryo you have injected doesn't actually implant in the womb of the mouse. But there are, from time to time of course, unpredicted and unexpected effects of this technology.

Now, one of the issues is whether or not it will be permissible to use this technology to attempt, not to eradicate certain disorders – because I don't believe that would be ever possible – but to reduce their incidence drastically. For example, if you take the population of Cyprus, there is in that population a disorder called beta-thalassaemia, which soaks up a huge proportion of that island's health care budget; probably around half of that budget has gone in the past on caring on the children that are either affected or dying of that disease, and who need regular blood transfusions. It's true, by various methods of social control, they have avoided many people marrying each other with these genes, but that doesn't work all the time. Supposing we could immunise, in effect, a population, by injecting the appropriate transgene, which I think might be possible; it may seem fanciful, but work that's currently going on suggests that we may be able to change the germ cells that are being produced by the male, so that any children which are produced would actually be, in effect, transgenic.

So, on the one hand, there is the possibility of disease limitation. But on the other hand, of course, there is the notion that we might use these same genetic approaches in the long distant future, to actually enhance our children. Why not, for example, consider genes that might promote intelligence, or strength, or what we perceive to be beauty, or aggression, if we wanted a soldier race? These are, I think, issues that are not discussed enough in our society, but probably are deserving of much more discussion, because I think that they will be scientifically possible, and I believe that they are issues of great, great importance.

One of the curious things is that, as humans, we are at least in part defined by our genetic make-up; we are different from other animals, because of our genetic structure. If we change that genetic structure are we still human, and if we are not, given that we regard ourselves being built in the image of God, and that our basic moral values, our respect for human life is based on the notion that we are made on the image of God, do we still have a respect for human life, and do we therefore have a respect for the people who are enhanced, or for the people who might be a subclass, who are not enhanced? I think there are some very interesting issues there that we might want to explore this evening.

There's a woodcut by Peter Breughel, which is about 450 years old, that is in the Kunstmuseum in Berlin, which shows the alchemist in his study, and he is experimenting with his assistants in the middle of the picture, trying to transmute base metals into gold. In the centre of that picture – you may well know it – his wife is sitting with an empty purse pouring money out, because the research grants for the elixir of life have run out. And it was a long time, and I didn't really understand this woodcut; it's called 'Algemist', a pun on the word 'Alchemist', and 'algemist' in Flemish also means 'all is lost'/'all has miscarried'. And what is interesting is that at the back of the woodcut are three children, one of whom has got the coal scuttle on his head, and they are scavenging in the cupboard at the back of the laboratory. And there's a wonderful medieval device in that picture – and I suggest you go and look at it, because it's in so many books – the window, and you see through the window, of course, the future, and in the window those three children are being led into the poor house. And I think what Breughel is suggesting is that we should beware of allowing our technology to subsume everything, and in particular, the most important thing that we have to remember is how our technology impinges on the next generation of humans.

Chapter 5

Staying human (2)

Richard Harries

Before coming to some specific issues I will say something, very briefly, about my general approach to this subject. First, the increasing number of possibilities open to us are an awesome *human* responsibility. This may seem obvious, but it contrasts with the view which suggests that it is God alone who deals with matters of life and death. God does indeed deal with them, but he deals with them through us human beings whom he has gifted with intelligence and skill. Lord Winston referred to our 'God-given tools of knowledge'. The capacity to interact with nature belongs to the very essence of what it is to be a human being. And there is no essential difference, for example, between somatic gene therapy and transplants. Both involve intervention in natural processes. The Bible says that the physician is to be honoured, and it singles out in particular our capacity to use the things of the earth to make medicines.[1] The principle enshrined there goes beyond pharmacy to include the many ways in which nature is harnessed or manipulated to service human ends.

Second, although amazing new possibilities are opening up for us, not everything that could be done should be done. There is a wisdom enshrined in nature that it is foolish to ignore. In recent decades we have been jolted into this truth by a growing awareness of the damage we have been doing to the environment and the ecosystems of the world. This has given rise to the precautionary principle. What is true in relation to the natural world is even more crucial when it comes to the human person. For life began on earth some three billion years ago and it is by a series of tiny, incremental steps through the mechanisms of replication, variation and selection that we are here tonight. The three billion bases of our genes in the human body, not to mention all the amazingly complex, co-operative organisms that make up the human frame, mean that we have an extraordinary ability to adapt and survive. This three billion years of careful adaptation, its built-in wisdom, suggests that it is sometimes right to go with the grain of nature rather than intervening.

So staying human at this time of extraordinary medical advance means both using our God-given capacities to interact with natural processes for human well-being, and at the same time having the humility to respect the built in wisdom in the given-ness of things.

The first and most fundamental fact about our time is the vast increase in knowledge and the ethical implications of this. The Human Genome Project, as a result of which every gene in the human body will be sequenced, had been expected to complete its task by 2003. Now just this week there are reports that a commercial organisation, Celera, will do so by June. I believe that this knowledge and its associated technologies is bringing about a shift in perspective in our time as fundamental as the theory of evolution did for the late Victorians. It will more and more shape the way we think and decide.

First, it is likely to make our lifespan much more certain. Of course we already know that certain conditions run in families – types of breast cancer, a propensity to heart attacks and so on – but we mostly live our life on the WHTM principle, that it 'won't happen to me'. With the vast increase in knowledge of our genetic make-up, a knowledge that is still in its infancy, we could become much more certain of when, barring accidents, we will die. Samuel Beckett wrote that we are 'born astride the grave'.[2] This truth will have a new precision. Some writers – understandably enough in relation to conditions like Huntington's chorea – take the view that genetics may tell us many things it may be better not to know. As has been written, 'the new genetics is making certainty, unattractive though it may often turn out to be, an option for more and more of us'.[3] Certainty about succumbing to a particular disease at a particular time, the certainty of death at a particular age. There is a sense of being fated or doomed in such sentiments, but I want to challenge that implication. We all know people who, given a few months to live, have lived to the full, perhaps in a way that has been richer, more vital and, indeed, life enhancing for others than many years before of measuring out life in a coffee spoon. A sculptor works with a particular piece of stone, a painter with a specific canvas. It is in wrestling with the particular, with quite specific constraints and definite boundaries, that art is produced. The same is true of life. So I wish to challenge the view that this vast increase in knowledge, leading to certainty in so many spheres where in the past there had been only uncertainty, will lead to fatalism. The human spirit is not made like that. Constraints, boundaries, limits can all act to liberate the potential we have within us to be truly human.

There are, however, serious implications at once ethical, social and political of this new certainty in its effect on health care and insurance. Already in the United States, one-third of all applicants for health insurance are refused and for all others all pre-existing conditions, whether reported or not, are excluded. This suggests that we are moving to a time in which only a few healthy and a few unhealthy but wealthy individuals will be able to obtain insurance for health care. The case for universal State-provided health care becomes even stronger.

Yet, secondly and paradoxically, while much will be made more certain, more choices will be open to us. We are becoming more aware of the ubiquity of inborn disease. In Britain one in thirty children is born with a genetic problem of some kind: a third of people who are blind are blind for genetic reasons: one in two of those who are severely mentally handicapped have an inherited condition. As Professor Steve Jones has put it, 'we each have at least one genetical skeleton in the cupboard'.[4]

At the moment pre-natal diagnosis (PND) allows some severe conditions to be identified. But the only choice open to the mother is to abort the foetus or continue with the pregnancy. In Sardinia nine out of ten of those at risk from of having a baby born with thalassaemia choose to end the pregnancy. In Denmark, where there has been systematic testing for older mothers, there has been a five-fold decrease in the number of children born with Down's Syndrome. Within ten years there will be tests for a thousand inherited diseases but the choice open to mothers on this basis is a stark one.

Now with pre-implantation genetic diagnosis (PGD) it will be increasingly possible for couples with a family history of a particular disease to ensure that only a genetically normal embryo is planted in the womb. The Human Fertilisation and Embryology Authority and the Advisory Committee on Genetic Testing have recently issued a consultation document on pre-implantation genetic diagnosis with a whole range of questions, all of which have an ethical dimension. For example, they ask:

> *Should guidance distinguish between PGD for genes that are highly predictive of a serious disorder and those where the genetic component is more complex? Should the use of PGD for any indication be the subject of clinical judgement, and as such left to practitioners and individual patients to decide?*[2]

Some people who strongly support PGD as a way of helping parents have children without serious genetic disorders are nevertheless concerned about this medical technology when it is combined with genetic engineering. It raises the spectre of fabricated man, of designer babies, of parents wanting children of a particular sex or build or intelligence or so on. A crucial switch would be made from the elimination of a faulty gene to ensuring that the child had genes of a particular sort, a sort which, in the judgement of their parents, enhanced life. In the United States the general public is much more enthusiastic about this possibility than geneticists or doctors, who are properly cautious on a number of grounds. There is, for example, what has been termed the tyranny of the normal. Would someone who would only grow to four foot be regarded as unacceptable, and if so why? Do we really want fashions in children as we have fashions in clothes? Theologians tend to distinguish between replacing faulty genes and replacing perfectly adequate ones to improve some characteristic: between redeeming the world (if you like, what Jewish rabbis of old called *Tikum olam* – repairing the universe) on the one hand and enhancing it on the other. This distinction is not quite as clear as it might sound. If someone who is slightly below normal IQ is brought up to normal through genetic manipulation, does this count as repair or enhancement? Nevertheless it is a rough-and-ready distinction that could at least alert us to the danger of genetic manipulation based simply on passing cultural fashions.

A more subtle and profound objection, based on a respect for the otherness of another person, has been put forward by Lord Habgood.[3] Although parents do, of course, seek to influence their children in all kinds of ways, they aim to treat them as individuals not as objects. This includes an element of given-ness about personality, which is accepted by both parents and children. The problem is not genetic manipulation as such or even the destruction of the embryo, but how genetic manipulation would affect the relationship between child and parent, if the child grows up knowing it has been designed by his or her parent to be a particular type, muscular or blond, slim or tall, or whatever. That child might very well come to resent the way he or she was and see only self-gratification in the parents' choice.

When we move away from manipulating particular cells to germ line therapy – changing the make-up of ovum or sperm or newly fertilised embryo so that when the person is grown and also reproduces, changes will be reproduced in future generations – other ethical considerations emerge, not least the question of consent. For though none of us asked to be born, there is a given-ness about who we are that we have to accept whether we like it or not. One age or culture could start to design children in ways their descendants might find totally unacceptable, unacceptable on perhaps moral and political grounds. And if they did not find it unacceptable but had been so conditioned as to accept without thinking that, let us say, obedience in a fascist state is the normal state of affairs, then we have entered the world of George Orwell and Aldous Huxley that most of us would find utterly repugnant.

There is also the point I made right at the beginning, about the wisdom that has been accumulated in nature over three billion years. It is not just a question of assessing particular risks, because we can never foresee all the risks, but the fear that through drastic intervention we could undo or undermine that special capacity to adapt and survive under so many conditions that it has taken us so long to achieve.

As long ago as the seventeenth century the French encyclopaedist Diderot envisaged in a laboratory a lot of little pots in which human beings would be grown.

The objection to this heady vision is not that it is illegitimate to meddle in the creation of life. We do that already even with the use of contraceptives and our capacity to do so will increase exponentionally in the decades ahead. It is that this capacity to interact with nature for human well-being needs to go with a deep respect for the grain of nature which, after all, has brought us where we are. This is not, I hope, simply fear of the unknown or innate conservatism but a proper regard for the wisdom built into the grain of things.

I now come, finally, to what is for many the crucial ethical question, namely the status of the embryo. The *Catechism of the Catholic Church* says:

> *Human life must be respected and protected absolutely from the moment of conception. From the first moment of existence, a human being must be recognised as having the rights of a person – among which is the inviolable right of every innocent being to life.*[7]

This is a view that is seriously held by a good many other people as well, who would not regard themselves as either Catholics or Christians. Those who don't take this view would argue that the respect properly due to what is potential may not be the same as the absolute respect that is due to what is fully developed. For example, we make a distinction between the thousands of acorns that fall from an oak tree and the fully grown oak. Another point which many would regard as ethically significant is that as many as three-quarters of the eggs that are fertilised are lost, most of them before they implant in their mother's womb, about a week after conception. Moreover, at least half of the fertilised eggs that miscarry are normal. This does not mean that because nature is prodigal we can be as well. Rather, as Professor Dunston has written:

> *Upon this waste, medical intervention imposes an economy. If successful it provides a baby where otherwise there would be none. The genetic information stored in the cells can be read: what is thus learned can be ordered into knowledge; knowledge can be put to beneficial, life saving use. The argument is not that because nature is prodigal we may be prodigal; because so much life or potential life is lost, one more does not matter. It is the reverse. It is that nature's prodigality is turned to creative use; natural loss is lessened, albeit to a minute degree.*[8]

For these and other reasons many Christians accepted the recommendations of the Warnock Report, which has now passed into law, that research on embryos should be allowed up to 14 days, though there has been a division about whether it is only spare embryos that should be used for research or whether they might be created specially for that purpose. Nevertheless, the status of the pre-implantation embryo is important. Professor Banner has argued that too much discussion of these matters that claim to be ethical consists only of an assessment of risks, costs and benefits. But, as he rightly points out, before we assess, for example, whether hanging is a deterrent, there is the prior question about whether it is ever right to take life.[9] Whatever answer one gives – the Catholic one that the embryo has to be accorded all the respect due to a fully developed human life or a respect that falls short of this – the question of status is important in itself before any question arises about the risks and benefits of research.

All this now bears on the subject of cloning. Everyone is agreed that cloning of embryos for reproduction purposes should continue to be banned. The question at issue therefore is using nuclear replacement technology for therapeutic purposes. This is not at present allowed, though some believe it should be. This 'therapeutic cloning', which I know Lord Winston regards as an inappropriate term and which he would prefer to call 'directed cell culture', offers the possibility of manufacturing cells useful for therapeutic purposes.

Those who object to this procedure do so not only because they regard the embryo, even before 14 days, as worthy of the respect we accord to a newborn baby, but also because that embryo – that potential person – would be treated as a means to something else, as an object. As has been said:

> It envisages creating something that has the capacity to become an adult human being, in the knowledge that we would then redirect it to become, in effect, a source of human spare parts.[10]

Some would argue that whatever the benefits this might bring in the way of treating diseases in other human beings, this would represent a profound change in what it is considered right to do with an embryo. The Warnock Report in 1984 said that the embryo should be accorded 'a special status'.[11] If – instead of proceeding to differentiate into the combination of cell types that make up a baby – the embryo is allowed to produce only certain kinds of cells which would then be copied for as long as possible in a laboratory, is this compatible with that 'special status'?

These are questions that are both profound and unresolved.

To sum up. I suggested as part of a general approach to these matters that our capacity to interact with nature to harness or manipulate it is part of our God-given human responsibility belonging to the very essence of what it is to be a human being. At the same time, there is a wisdom enshrined in nature that it is foolish to ignore. The main characteristic of our time is the extraordinary increase in knowledge, particularly knowledge of our genetic make-up. This is likely to have two effects. On the one hand, it will make some conditions, perhaps even our lifespan, more certain. I argue that this need not necessarily lead to a sense of being fated, because genuine human freedom always works within particular boundaries and constraints. On the other hand, this knowledge, together with developing technology, means that many more choices will be open to us in the future. It is already becoming apparent in relation to pre-implantation genetic diagnosis. When *in vitro* techniques are combined with genetic engineering, extraordinary possibilities could open out.

There are no fundamental ethical difficulties about somatic gene therapy, provided it is given on the basis of informed consent. Germ line therapy, however, in which the genetic make-up of offspring, whether of this generation or subsequent ones, is changed, raises major questions. It is not the genetic manipulation itself that is the problem but the effect this might have upon the relationship of children and their parents or forebears. Children could come to resent particular characteristics that they had been given and come to regard them only as expressions of parental self-gratification.

The possibility of repairing or replacing faulty genes offers real hope for many conditions and is to be warmly welcomed. However, the prospect of replacing perfectly adequate genes in order to enhance some characteristic exposes us to the danger of creating people to reflect some passing cultural fashion, perhaps even one with unpleasant political overtones.

Finally, there is the status of the embryo, which from an ethical point of view needs to be considered as a question in its own right before any consideration of risks, costs and benefits of research. The Warnock Report said that it should be accorded 'a special status'. A further question arises as to whether this special status is compatible with using it for tissue engineering.

I believe that the genetic revolution is creating a shift in perspective in our time as fundamental as the theory of evolution did for the late Victorians. This does not point to genetic determinism. It is interesting how strongly the present scientific community rejects that and champions the capacity of human beings to function as a reflective, self-directing whole. It is our continuing capacity to do that in the face of unprecedented medical advances and to reflect, as we are doing here, on their ethical implications that ensures we stay human.

References

1. 'Honour the physician with the honour due to him … for the Lord created him … for healing comes from the most high … the Lord created medicines from the earth, and a sensible man will not despise them … he gave skill to men that he might be glorified in his marvellous works. By them he heals and takes away pain; the pharmacist makes of them a compound.' Ecclesiasticus, 38.
2. Dunstan G R, Seller M J, eds. *The status of the human embryo*. King Edward's Hospital Fund for London and OUP: 1988.
3. Banner M. Christian anthropology at the beginning and end of life. In: *Christian ethics and contemporary moral problems*. Cambridge University Press: 1999, chapter 2.

Chapter 6

Personal freedom or public health? (1)

Bruce Charlton

Public health and personal freedom in conflict

Public health and personal freedom are frequently in conflict. Public health is, after all, a branch of government, with an agenda that shares the perspective, the virtues and the vices of government. It is not unusual that individuals find their liberty, values and aspirations thwarted by governments.

I will make a case for greater individual freedom in relation to health. Using examples drawn from psychiatry, I will demonstrate that public health often stands in the path of personal satisfaction, fulfilment and creativity; and will argue for greater freedom of access to medications. In particular, I will make the case for the availability on request of potentially life-enhancing pyschotropic drugs such as antidepressants.

The discussion will focus on a specific example: one of the most powerful of psychologically active drugs, a drug that is widely and cheaply available in our society – and a drug that has been used by most of the people who are likely to be reading this. I mean alcohol.

The public health perspective

Public health involves putting the health of the group as a higher priority than the interests of individuals. Whether or not this is justifiable must be argued case by case.[1]

A classic, and justifiable, public health intervention might be quarantining a person suffering from a potentially fatal infectious disease. Individual freedom is sacrificed, but perhaps the whole community may be saved. Even here one can see the potential dangers of public health. Its operation is often intrinsically coercive, and the calculus by which the well-being of the group is balanced against that of the individual typically leaves considerable scope for disagreement, as well as scope for partiality and prejudice.

In psychiatry a similar argument might be deployed to prevent the availability of a drug which – it was believed – rendered the user a homicidal maniac. In such a situation, the well-being of the group would presumably dictate that the freedom of the individual to determine what went into his or her own body could reasonably be curtailed.

But typically, public health issues are much less clear cut. For example, the sacrifice may involve not a minority but the majority of the population – and the benefits may accrue to just a few. Some instances of immunisation involve inflicting pain, inconvenience and risk of side effects on the bulk of the population in order that disease be prevented in a minority. This may indeed be justifiable, for instance when immunisation led to the eradication of smallpox, but there is a large ethical grey area in which the balance of benefits versus harm is uncertain.

In sum, there is a tendency for public health to be conscripted by politics, and to coerce the citizen – and to become a kind of 'medical police' to enforce the will of the State.[2] Public health policies require continual watching with a sceptical eye.

The public health perspective on alcohol

From the public health perspective alcohol is a bad thing. Alcohol has, of course, great potential for harm. For instance, in a book entitled *Alcohol and the public health*, which was issued by the Faculty of Public Health, there is just *one sentence* on the benefits of drinking![3] The dangers of alcohol consumption have been extensively documented in the statistics of road traffic accidents, violence, suicide and physical disease.[4,5]

Because of this catalogue of harm, the probable major public health benefit of drinking alcohol – a reduced rate of heart attacks – has been denied or ignored by official public health channels. However, despite the fact that heart disease was for many decades the major killer in the UK, few public health professionals will take the risk of being seen to encourage drinking.

So, to the public health branch of government, alcohol is bad and public health sees alcohol in terms of diminishing harm, e.g. by punitive taxation and restrictions on availability.[3] On the other hand, to the fiscal branch of government, the taxes raised by alcohol sales are good. In practice, government policies towards alcohol are the outcome of these and other competing interests. The individual pleasures and social benefits of alcohol simply do not enter the equation – except insofar as they impinge on electability.

And in this respect, alcohol is representative of the public health attitude to psychologically active substances in general. When it comes to defining policy, the overriding goal is to minimise harm,[5] where harm is defined in terms of preventing positive, objective, quantifiable public consequences such as rates of accidents, suicide and violence. Private 'goods' that may result from pyschotropic drugs – goods such as increased happiness, sociability, and human fulfilment in general – these are simply not a part of the calculus since they are private, subjective and incalculable.

Psychiatry and public health

The public health perspective on alcohol reflects the perspective on psychiatry, which sees mental illness in terms of its objective and interpersonal manifestations such as suicides and assaults, and their implications for expenditure. But a population locked into a negative state of docile low-grade misery would be invisible to public health, since such people present no public problem.[6]

When Henry Thoreau accurately observed that the mass of men lead lives of 'quiet desperation',[7] he was writing against his background in Puritan New England in the early nineteenth century. Puritanism may be characterised by an overriding imperative to avoid the risk of harm, specifically the need to avoid public manifestations of sin. The blind spot of puritanism is to avoid the risk of personal sin at no matter what cost in terms of lost opportunities for personal virtue. In this sense, public health psychiatry is almost inevitably driven by that species of puritanism that Gerald Klerman has astutely called 'pharmacological Calvinism'.[8]

The general thrust of specifically psychiatric public health therefore focuses almost exclusively upon the dangers presented by people suffering psychiatric illness, and the dangers of drugs and other interventions used to treat it. Indeed, since the specialty of psychiatry developed from the need for asylum, this puritanical deformity affects the whole subject to some extent. The need for treatment is prioritised in terms of its effect of reducing the incidence of these public dangers. For instance, the only numerical target of the UK government's *Health of the nation* White Paper of 1992 was reduction of suicide rates.[9] Similarly, recent UK debate about 'care in the community' legislation focuses upon whether current rules provide adequate protection to the public, and to a lesser extent protection to the psychiatric patient.

Public health has no interest in whether a person is leading a fulfilled life – subjective aspects of mental health are invisible. So long as people do not try to kill themselves or others and do not make a nuisance of themselves, that counts as a successful outcome. In a nutshell, from the public health perspective psychiatry has the puritanical tendency to sacrifice individual happiness, fulfilment and creativity whenever this sacrifice contributes to the goals of preventing harm – that is, to sacrifice human possibility in pursuit of risk-prevention.

Personal psychiatry has very different priorities, since it is precisely concerned with the fine texture of everyday life seen from within; hence it is dominated by subjective goods and individual satisfactions. From the personal perspective, people seek more from life than the negative benefits of minimising risk of danger and avoiding being a nuisance. As individuals, we are dissatisfied by lives of 'quiet desperation', and will often take advantage of opportunities offering the prospect of escape from dullness and despondency. Better still, we may seize any realistic chances of the positive goods of happiness and creativity. And many people choose to avail themselves of psychologically active agents in pursuit of this goal.

The psychotropic effects of alcohol

Alcohol is probably the most powerful of widely available psychotropic drugs. Its effects vary between people and according to dose. In high doses alcohol produces intoxication, stupor, coma and eventually death; in lower doses, its effects may be benign and life-enhancing. Indeed, the Nobel prize-winning psychopharmacologist Arvid Carlsson has said:

> *Alcohol has done more good than bad to mankind. I am convinced of that. There is so much that has come out of the increased interaction between individuals because of alcohol. Some individuals have had to pay very much for this, but mankind has done very well I think.*[10]

However, the risk of harm is public, objective and quantifiable, while the benefits are typically private, subjective and cannot be given a numerical value.

All drugs are double-edged agents in the sense that any treatment capable of affecting the body powerfully enough to do good, is in principle also capable of affecting the body in a harmful way. All effective treatments have significant side effects, and only useless treatments are harmless. But many psychotropic drugs have this quality of objective harms but only subjective benefits, so that from a public health perspective it is tempting to limit the availability and usage of these agents.

Opiates are a good example of the phenomenon: opium derivatives such as heroin are at the same time one of the greatest boons to humankind, by virtue of their tremendously powerful pain-relieving action; and one of the greatest and most tragic plagues in history, by their potential for dependence and addiction when abused. The ill effects of heroin are more objective than its benefits. The puritanical response, adopted in the United States, is to enforce abstinence. This results in making the use of heroin illegal – even for medical purposes.

In other words, the attempt to reduce the public health risk of addiction is regarded as more important than the benefits of alleviating the subjectively experienced pain of individual people. The unintended consequence has been that the only people in the USA with access to heroin are drug addicts. Patients suffering extreme pain from terminal disease must make do with often inferior substitutes.

Sacrificing clinical medicine to public health

At a 'milder' level of pain, recent legislation in the UK has meant that aspirin and paracetamol are sold over the counter only in packs of 32 tablets maximum, and in 'blister' packaging in order to deter overdosing and reduce the national statistics of attempted suicide.

This strategy of reducing the availability of drugs (less than three days' supply of aspirin can be purchased in one go) and enormously increasing its cost (due to expensive packaging and larger overheads) appears to have been successful. Some good has come of it: paracetamol overdosages are indeed less common, and the pharmaceutical companies and pharmacists have had their profit margins enhanced. But the consequences in terms of increased pain (and reduced wealth) experienced by the tens of millions of people who use these drugs has not been taken into account. The problem is that these consequences *cannot* be taken into account, no matter how real and intrusive they are to the people who experience them.

This raises the dilemma of public health in its starkest form: tens of millions of people have suffered preventable pain in order to deter, lets say, some hundreds or thousands of people from taking overdoses with paracetamol or aspirin. Taken to its logical conclusion, access to painkillers should be made so inconvenient and expensive that overdoses are impossible. Even as things stand, the public health imperative to prevent harm has overwhelmed the clinical imperative of medicine to do good, and the reason that this has been allowed to happen is that the harm is statistical (and a *Health of the nation* managerial target), while the benefit is subjective.

The uses of alcohol

Alcohol is yet another double-edged pharmacological agent. Indeed, it is a mistake to regard alcohol as one drug. More accurately, it can be regarded as several drugs – according to dose and context, and the purpose for which it is taken.

Alcohol is not *just* a drug, since it is a flavouring element in some of the most complexly enjoyable foods and drinks: beer, cider, wine, whisky, and so on. Indeed, almost all complexly enjoyable drinks contain psychoactive drugs, for instance the caffeine in tea and coffee. I do not know why this should be, but adult humans seem to get a particularly *refined* pleasure from 'acquiring the taste' for mild toxins that children reject. For example, mouldy 'Blue Stilton' is perhaps the finest of cheeses, 'well-hung' game such as pheasant or venison is actually putrefying by the time it is cooked, and bitter dark chocolate is regarded as more sophisticated than the sweeter white or milk varieties. So, one major reason for drinking alcohol is that people like the taste of alcoholic drinks.

Another reason that people drink alcohol is, of course, to become intoxicated as a positive objective in its own right. When intoxication is the object, people don't much mind what the drink tastes like. I have spoken with Scandinavians who distilled a brew made from a fermented solution of sugar, yeast and tomato ketchup. Some people from central Europe will even drink schnapps.

In other words, some of the people, some of the time, drink alcohol to produce a delirious state of brain impairment, arriving at which they find to be a gratifying process. Intoxication of this sort may be a kind of happy holiday from the real world, albeit the happiness is short-lived and usually followed by that holiday-in-hell we call a hangover.

Benefits of alcohol

But aside from its effects in flavouring and as a pleasurable intoxicant, there are at least three other reasons for taking alcohol as a psychoactive drug; and all of these reasons have the objective of enhancing life. The first is as a hypnotic, to promote sleep. The second is to take alcohol as a kind of 'antidepressant' or painkiller. The third is to use alcohol as an anti-anxiety agent, particularly to reduce shyness, increase confidence and lubricate social intercourse.

From a narrowly public health perspective, these psychopharmacological benefits of alcohol are almost invisible. Whether someone is shy, has a good night's sleep or is miserable are matters of supreme indifference to the Government, except insofar as a population of shy, insomniac miseries are probably easier to control than a population of confident, well-rested and motivated people.

The first point to emphasise is that sleep, happiness and confidence are perfectly reasonable attributes for people to seek – we are not talking about drug-crazed ecstasies. So, we need to avoid the easy option of pharmacological Calvinism and advocating abstinence, since this would only diminish dangers by eliminating the possibility of benefit.

The benefits of alcohol can be examined and evaluated. If people want to achieve these benefits, and it is decided that alcohol is a suboptimal or excessively dangerous strategy for achieving them, then it behoves us to suggest some other alternatives to alcohol that achieve the desired effect, either with better efficacy or at lower risk.

1. Hypnotic

Alcohol is sometimes used as a hypnotic to promote sleep. There are two ways in which this is commonly done – one benign, the other harmful. In low doses, and when getting off to sleep is the problem and staying asleep once you are asleep is not a problem, occasional use of alcohol as a hypnotic is reasonable, for example the hot whisky toddy when suffering from a cold.

But alcohol is quite rapidly eliminated from the body so will seldom produce a full night's sleep.[11] If taken in a large dose to 'knock you out', alcohol does not so much promote sleep as produce anaesthesia, and anaesthesia does not yield the restorative benefits of true sleep. Indeed, when the alcohol begins to wear off there is usually a rebound characterised by shallow sleep with vivid and unpleasant dreams and early awakening.

Poor sleep is a very common complaint, probably due to the noisy, tense, crowded lives we lead that require so much planning and worrying, and where we are ruled by the clock rather than the spontaneous rhythms of the body. For instance, recordings of brain waves indicate that an early afternoon siesta is programmed into humans, yet how many people are able to fit a post-lunch nap into their working schedules?

Humans *can* get by on just a few hours sleep per night and can struggle through a lifetime of low-grade fatigue. But if we are not talking about mere *survival*, but instead about the possibility of leading a fulfilling and creative life, then it may be that sustained and satisfying sleep is necessary for that personal goal.

If alcohol is a relatively ineffective and potentially addictive hypnotic, then we need to consider the alternative. Sleep can be promoted by a wide range of drugs, but a natural-feeling, restorative and satisfying sleep is much harder to obtain, even when the full range of modern pharmacology is available. The standard sleeping tablets are not strikingly good at providing a satisfying sleep except in the short term, probably because they distort the natural pattern of brain waves that seem to be needed to produce the benefits of sleep. My hunch is that some of the unusual antidepressants, like trazodone or mianserin, hormones such as melatonin, or the new atypical neuroleptic drugs, like risperidone and olanzepine, may produce a better quality of sleep than the currently used agents, although all have significant side effects.[12]

In the longer term, more studies need to be done in which sleeping medications are evaluated by people's subjective satisfaction at the quality of their night's sleep, rather than by objective measures of how many hours of unconsciousness they produce. Until then, each individual would need to try different agents in different doses to discover what best suited them.

2. Antidepressant painkiller

Alcohol is sometimes – implicitly – used as a kind of antidepressant; its function being to allow the drinker to *escape* from a state of misery. This antidepressant use of alcohol is equivalent to using it as a psychological 'painkiller' or analgesic. Indeed, alcohol is sometimes used as a physical painkiller. Before the invention of anaesthetics, alcohol was taken prior to painful operations, and even nowadays some people with chronic, intractable pain or depression resort to drinking to excess as a way of seeking relief.

Unfortunately, to achieve the effect of dulling the mind to pain, alcohol must be taken in large enough doses to produce a significant degree of intoxication. Substantial impairment of mental function is inevitable, and physical damage and addiction are probable in the long term.

This is how alcohol is traditionally used, or abused, in high latitude northern European societies such as Finland, Scotland and Newcastle-upon-Tyne – drink is taken to the point of intoxication, or not at all. The population is divided into teetotal abstainers and binge drinkers. My hunch is that this bingeing versus abstention pattern of alcohol use may be related to the fact that high latitudes have a high incidence of seasonal affective disorder caused by the short hours of daylight in winter producing episodes of winter and spring depression. This high prevalence of depression is 'self-treated' in a sub-sector of the population by dulling the mental pain through escaping into a state of intoxication or oblivion. But because of the social harms produced by this pattern of alcohol consumption, drinking becomes stigmatised and attitudes to it become polarised with the development of powerful temperance movements.[13]

But abstinence, although safer, is not necessarily a very happy alternative. In Protestant northern Europe, especially before the era of modern psychopharmacology, the majority of the population who abstained from alcohol tended to be introverted, dour and miserable, leading lives of puritanical self-denial and 'quiet desperation'. When alcohol is the only available antidepressant, a person's choice usually simplifies to a short, wild, violently emotional life of intermittent intoxication or a life of over-controlled low-grade misery and watery pleasure. The abstinence alternative is associated with a longer life – and it certainly *feels* like a longer life.

Neither abstinence nor binge drinking is an ideal response to depression. There are superior substitutes for alcohol as an antidepressant, agents that are both safer and more effective.[14] Indeed alcohol is a pretty ineffective antidepressant: short-acting and only relieving misery at the price of significant brain impairment.

My understanding of depression is that it is not so much a mood, as a physical state.[12,15] Depression is a feeling of *malaise* – of fatigue, heaviness, dull diffuse aches and pains and the de-motivating inability to experience or to anticipate long-term pleasurable emotions. This physical state prevents a person from feeling gratifying emotions and gradually drags the mood down. True antidepressants therefore probably work rather like a painkiller or analgesic, to relieve these physical sensations of fatigue, heaviness and pain.

So, the traditional antidepressant painkillers, such as imipramine and amitriptyline, which are powerful and long-acting analgesics, are a much better option than alcohol for treating depression without impairing mental function and they also tend to improve appetite and sleep. These traditional antidepressants do, however, produce unpleasant side effects in some people that outweigh their beneficial effects. It may be that other painkillers could be used to treat some of the malaise state of depression. For instance, simple analgesics available over the counter, such as aspirin, paracetamol or ibuprofen, and the mild opiate analgesics, such as codeine, may turn out to have a role as antidepressants.[12]

All antidepressants have side effects that may be troublesome, and there is always the problem of deliberate overdose. But they are probably a safer, more effective and less addictive alternative to alcohol. An individual person may decide that the subjective benefits outweigh the risks, and may find that life while taking antidepressants is more fulfilling than life without the drug.[16] In my opinion, whether or not to take antidepressants should generally be a matter of choice for the patient. The doctor would adopt an advisory role – except when treatment would be dangerous, when a veto may be exercised.[17]

3. Alcohol as an anxiolytic social lubricant

When used in small frequent doses, especially when taken with food, alcohol reduces anxiety and promotes sociability in many people.[11] Broadly speaking, this is how alcohol is used in southern European countries such as Spain. In Spain, drinks may be taken frequently but moderately throughout the day, with food (which slows alcohol absorption), and the drinker never shows signs of intoxication. Indeed, traditionally, Spanish men would regard slurring their words, uncoordinated action or uncontrolled behaviour as shameful, unmasculine behaviour leading to loss of reputation. So, in Spain most people drink, most of the time, yet very few get drunk. The contrast with northern European patterns of drinking is extreme.

Small frequent doses of alcohol are an effective treatment for shyness. And debilitating shyness, even the extreme form of social phobia, are very common in our mass industrial society populated largely by masses of strangers. Hence the use of alcohol as a social lubricant is, by and large, life-enhancing, especially since social relations are probably the single major source of human satisfaction.

So long as proper precautions are taken, this style of alcohol usage promotes a fulfilling human life. However, even modest alcohol consumption does produce a measurable impairment of some mental functions, and frequent doses are necessary to produce a sustained effect. In the long term, physical damage is a possibility and liver cirrhosis is common in countries such as Spain. So what are the alternatives?

The most straightforward alternative to alcohol is the benzodiazepine group of drugs such as diazepam (or Valium).[18] These share many of the disadvantages of alcohol in terms of being potentially addictive and prone to abuse, but they have the advantages of being longer acting and safer than alcohol – safer both in acute intoxicating doses, and in the long term. It seems clear that there are some people, although perhaps not very many, who are neither addicted to nor dependent on benzodiazepines, but whose lives are more satisfying when taking a small or occasional dose of these drugs.

More promising alternatives to alcohol as a social lubricant are some of the newer drugs marketed under the 'antidepressant' label, drugs such as fluoxetine (better known as Prozac) or paroxetine (Seroxat), which was recently licensed specifically for the treatment of social phobia and which has been shown in trials to improve social confidence even in normal non-depressed people.[19] When they work, and when side effects (that may be severe) are not significant, such drugs may diminish shyness and promote social interactions. Lives have been transformed for the better by diminishing pointless anxiety and allowing the emergence of a more relaxed and sociable personality and lifestyle.[15] This is not a dumb intoxication, but a new set of positive possibilities that can be life-enhancing – even profoundly so.

My belief is that drugs such as Prozac and Seroxat work as emotional buffers.[12] They do not alter normal emotions but prevent extreme swings of emotions. They are a kind of safety net that guards against overpowering negative emotions. This is often reassuring to shy persons who know that they will not be overwhelmed by panic or loss of control in social situations. On the down side, extreme positive emotions may be buffered as well as negative ones, so the up-swings of euphoric feelings that most of us get from being in love, and some of us get from exercise, may be diminished. And this may be unpleasant or too big a price to pay for many people.

Again, it is a matter of individual constitution, individual responses and preferences. Hence the decision whether or not to take the drug should be individual since only the individual can judge whether the benefits compensate for the side effects and risks.

Personal freedom

Alcohol is a drug of abuse, but not just a drug of abuse; nor is the use of alcohol necessarily an inappropriate exercise of human freedom. People use alcohol for good reasons as well as bad – to produce effects that are life-enhancing, as well as the more familiar life-escaping effects.

But there are potentially superior alternatives to alcohol, even where is it being used appropriately, for instance to reduce shyness. These alternatives may be safer and more effective – as well as cheaper. Yet typically alternative psychopharmacological agents are not readily available, except on prescription and only then when indicated by a formal psychiatric or medical diagnosis. Because of this link to mental illness, even when they are available and appropriate, the use of psychotropic drugs is stigmatised compared with alcohol.[20] The drug comes with the label of suffering a mental disorder, despite the fact that people without any detectable psychiatric disorder may benefit from taking such drugs – as is the case for antidepressants.

At present, people lack the freedom to optimise their personal health, largely because of the constraints of public health. The public health principle is to avoid harm, which implies restricting the access and availability of powerful psychotropic drugs because of their potential dangers, and these restrictions apply even when such agents may enhance life. This conflicts with the personal goal of maximising individual well-being.

In effect, we as individuals are not allowed to make the decision to take the risk of consuming, say, Prozac unless we are judged by a professional to be at some *greater* risk of harm because we are suffering from a formal psychiatric illness.[20] In other words, the risk benefit analysis is made *for* us, by other people – despite the radically incomplete information they have of potential and actual benefits, due to these being subjective. These scales are weighted in favour of abstinence. The public health perspective has a blind spot exactly where health matters most to each of us – our own subjective sense of well-being.

The consequence is an invisible plague of avoidable misery. Invisible, because it constitutes psychiatric symptoms with mainly private significance – malaise, misery, free-floating anxiety, social phobia, insomnia; avoidable, because these symptoms are left untreated for fear that their treatment may cause public health problems such as side effects, overdoses, addiction or other causes of excessive health service expenditure; and a plague, because there are millions of people whose lives subjectively feel blighted, who might, although there is no guarantee, find a pharmacological agent that would enable them to lead significantly happier, more creative lives.[12]

So, we are not talking about using drugs as euphoriants, we are talking about drugs that may increase the chance of human fulfilment through a diminution of pain and malaise, a more satisfying social life, more restorative sleep, and more energy and motivation to tackle the projects that make life worth living.[17] Such agents do not *make* someone happy, any more than taking aspirin makes you happy. Taking aspirin to treat a headache does not make you happy, but it is difficult to lead a fulfilled life when suffering a headache, and easier to be happy when the pain has been relieved. So, our concern is with agents that do not induce happiness; rather, they remove obstacles to happiness.

What applies specifically to psychiatric disease and psychotropic drugs applies generally to other diseases and other therapeutic agents. When health services are focused on public health they become dominated by objective factors, such as the statistics of morbidity and mortality. In such a framework it is likely that the personal and subjective aspects of health are neglected. Individual freedom is often overwhelmed by public health because it is so easy to ignore the misery of others or thwart their aspirations. Against each person's own misery is stacked the ignorance and indifference of the majority who are not so afflicted.

Greater access to pharmacological agents

At present, access to drugs is largely restricted to 'prescription only', except where it can be demonstrated that a drug's benefits in practice outweigh its dangers by a substantial margin. The onus of proof lies on those who wish to give the public access, and the default position is that access is denied.

In other words, the public is denied direct access to modern pharmacology: under the present system a sufferer has no right of access to agents that may relieve his or her suffering. For instance, a person in severe pain must convince a doctor of his or her condition in order to gain access to powerful painkillers. If the person in pain does not convince a doctor, or the doctor judges that the risk of providing pain relief outweighs the probable benefits, then the patient must continue to suffer.

But the principle can be reversed. The public could have access to all pharmacological agents except where it could be shown that this would be inappropriate. In other words, members of the public might demand the right to determine their own treatment – perhaps choosing to make exceptions where this right is suspended. Exceptions might be made in the case of children, or substances that are highly addictive, dangerous or toxic.

This situation is, of course, the one that existed until about 100 years ago.[20] Restricted public access to drugs is a relatively recent phenomenon. Prescription-only drug restrictions were originally introduced purely for controlling access to dangerously addictive agents such as cocaine and morphine. Now all drugs are treated as if they were dangerously addictive, and all adults treated as if they were dependent addicts.

Some people may wish to take the chance of the benefits of a drug, even when the odds are against them. For instance, a person in severe pain or other distress may choose to take considerable risks to escape this situation. Such a person might want pain relief even when this brought with it a small chance of addiction, since they may judge that a life dominated by pain is no life. The same applies to shyness, malaise and anxiety. These negative emotions may dominate the lives of people, thwart their aspirations, and they may feel that even a significant risk is worth taking in order to obtain relief.

Of course, such a policy would present significant dangers – all freedoms present dangers. Of course, it would be wise for patients to seek expert advice before ingesting powerful chemicals; it is easier to harm oneself than help oneself, and there is significant potential for injury from all agents that may do good. And of course there is the question of who pays for all this. But at the end of the day, the *principle* must surely be that individuals should be responsible for what they put into their own bodies, since each individual bears the brunt of both risks and benefits. If people wish to take risks with their bodies then they should be able to do so. The rest is logistics.

From the example of alcohol, it is overwhelmingly obvious that many people *wish* to use pharmacological means of shaping their lives, and indeed do so within the constraints of available and acceptable agents. Too often a question is framed about whether people should or should not avail themselves of psychotropic drugs in shaping their lives. But this is a mistaken emphasis, and it assumes that 'we' have a right to decide what drugs other people take and whether they 'deserve' to take them. The onus of proof needs to be reversed: what right do 'we' have to determine which chemicals other people put into their bodies? And why are people *prevented* from using drugs which they believe may benefit them?

Conclusion

In a world where psychiatric symptoms are endemic and where there are treatments that offer a significant chance of significant benefit, then the proper question should not be *whether* humans should use psychotropic drugs, but *how* humans should use psychiatric drugs.[12] This presupposes that people have access to such agents.

Not all drugs should be available on request, nor should all drugs be available unrestrictedly. But given the vast potential for subversion of public health by goals of expediency,[2] the essentially political nature of public health, and the way in which it can so easily be made to serve the interests of government against both individuals and populations, then individual freedom seems the best starting point for rational policy. Protection of freedom should be the fundamental postulate, and restrictions on freedom should require specific justification in each instance of restriction. The best safeguard against the abuse of public health is personal freedom.

It follows that the *primary* decisions in medicine should be based on criteria of personal health, not public health. And, at the bottom line, subjective experience is more important than objective statistics.

References

1. Charlton B G. Public health medicine: a different kind of ethics. *Journal of the Royal Society of Medicine* 1993; 86: 194–95.

2. Skrabanek P. *The death of humane medicine and the rise of coercive healthism.* London: Social Affairs Unit, 1994.

3. FPHM (Faculty of Public Health Medicine of the Royal College of Physicians). *Alcohol and the public health.* London: Macmillan, 1991.

4. Edwards G, Peters T J, editors. *Alcohol and alcohol problems.* Edinburgh: Churchill Livingstone, 1994.

5. Plant M, Single E, Stockwell T. *Alcohol: minimising the harm.* London: Free Association Books, 1997.

6. Pearce D. *Paradise engineering and the post-Darwinian transition.* 2000. http://www.post-darwinism.com/

7. Thoreau H D. *Walden.* Princeton, NJ: Princeton University Press, 1971 (modern edition; originally published in 1854).

8. Attributed.

9. Secretary of State for Health. *The health of the nation: a strategy for health in England.* London: HMSO, 1992.

10. Healy D. *The psychopharmacologists.* London: Chapman & Hall, 1996.

11. Leonard B E. *Fundamentals of psychopharmacology.* 2nd ed. Chichester: John Wiley & Sons, 1997.

12. Charlton B G. *Psychiatry and the human condition.* Oxford: Radcliffe Medical Press, 2000.

13. Levine H G. Temperance cultures. In: Lader M, Edwards G, Drummond D C, editors. *The nature of alcohol and drug-related problems.* Oxford: Oxford University Press, 1992.

14. Pearce D. *The responsible parent's guide to healthy mood-boosters for all the family.* 2000. http://www.biopsychiatry.com/

15. Charlton B G. The malaise theory of depression: major depressive disorder is sickness behavior and antidepressants are analgesic. *Medical Hypotheses* 2000; 54: 1–5.

16. Kramer P. *Listening to Prozac.* London: Fourth Estate, 1994.

17. Charlton B G. Psychopharmacology and the human condition. *Journal of the Royal Society of Medicine* 1998; 91: 599–601.

18. Healy D. *Psychiatric drugs explained.* 2nd ed. London: Mosby, 1997.

19. Knutson B, Wolkowitz O M, Cole S W. Selective alteration of personality and social behavior by serotonergic intervention. *American Journal of Psychiatry* 1998; 155: 543–47.

20. Healy D. *The antidepressant era.* Cambridge, MA: Harvard University Press, 1998.

Chapter 7

Personal freedom or public health? (2)

Peter Budetti

Overview/abstract

This paper makes an argument favouring more government involvement in promoting and protecting health, at both the individual and higher levels. In attempting to balance the rights involved, the most fundamental trade-off is the tension between personal freedom and public health. Protecting the public's health may indeed require substantial constraints on the individual, and any such constraints should provoke serious attention to individual rights that might be threatened. But individual behaviour is only one of many factors affecting health. Thus, interference with individual freedom alone – however well considered and respectful of individual rights – cannot accomplish the protection of population health. Other influences on health need to be recognised, and governmental action is appropriate with respect to many of them.

Imposing interventions that address health determinants beyond individual behaviour, however, raises several problems, two of which are explored here.

First, interventions above the individual level implicate rights that go beyond individual freedom. This is illustrated in this paper by considering in depth the issue of environmental degradation as a by-product of economic development, which has prompted many calls for restricting development to protect the environment and in turn to protect health. Controls on development, however, can be viewed as fundamentally unfair to underdeveloped populations who have a 'right to development' and who may well gain health through improved socio-economic status even as they degrade the environment.

Second, because many higher-order interventions can be effective only if they are imposed on a multinational basis, such controls immediately encounter all of the barriers to international co-operation. This is illustrated in this paper by the on-going struggle over hormone-stimulated beef and genetically modified agricultural products. The barriers faced by multinational efforts to deal with such issues range from concerns for national sovereignty and interests to divergent cultural beliefs about science.

The analysis developed here suggests an approach that considers governmental controls within a context of a wide range of rights (not just personal freedom) and the net effect of various influences on health (in which even environmentally harmful development may improve population health). This analysis leads to the conclusion that the greater level of government involvement needed to protect health may take many forms, including reasonable limitations on personal liberty as well as protection of 'negative' rights, such as freedom of economic development, where the net result is improved health overall. This expanded formulation will require at least the following:

- an analytical framework that assesses the net impact on health against the interference with rights
- procedures that accommodate divergent attitudes toward science and health
- a set of enforcement tools to carry out such governmental actions
- continuous monitoring to avoid disastrous long-term consequences.

Basic formulation: individual freedom and public health

The issue for this conference, as is the case more generally in the literature, has been framed in terms of seeking to identify the level of interference with individual behaviour that is tolerable for the sake of public health. Indeed, the phrase 'personal freedom or public health' suggests that the two are mutually exclusive to some substantial degree. The outer limits of this tension are represented, on the one hand, by those who maintain the classic libertarian perspective of minimal governmental action, and on the other hand, by those who promote vigorous intervention to uphold a right to health and health care.

The minimalist, libertarian perspective sanctions governmental action only to uphold 'negative' rights, such as autonomy, property, and the right to participate in the market-place without interference from force or deceit.[1] The consequences can be extreme: Epstein, for example, argues that hospitals should be able to refuse treatment to individuals who have brought ill health upon themselves.[2]

The antipathy to government constraints on personal liberty runs deep. Even though polls show that 75–90 per cent of the American population favour such laws, motorcycle enthusiasts prevailed on the Congress to repeal a federal statute pressuring states to require helmets, and on the Governor of California to veto a state law. "'When states attempt to control behavior, many people feel that is onerous," said Eric J Lundquist, legislative affairs director for the American Motorcyclist Association, an organization of enthusiasts with headquarters in Westerville, Ohio.'[3]

The American movie star, Gary Busey, spent some time crusading for individual rights against public interference – with substantial consequences for his own health. He achieved fame by starring in *The Buddy Holly Story* in the late 1970s, and has had frequent roles as a movie 'heavy' ever since. A story in the *New York Times* in 1989, shortly after he suffered head injuries in a motorcycle accident, reported that 'Mr Busey … was riding without a helmet, which would have offered some protection when his head struck a curb in Culver City, Calif[ornia]. In fact, he had helped bring about a veto of legislation last year that would have required him to wear one.'[4]

At the other end of the spectrum are those who advocate far more restrictive public health measures to fulfil various rights to health and health care that may require numerous government constraints on personal freedom. For example, proponents of a national health care system in the US (the lack of which remains a source of great consternation for many of us in the States, and of substantial amusement and bewilderment among the inhabitants of the rest of the developed world) recognise the need to impose on personal liberty to some degree to create such a system. President Clinton's health reform plan in 1993 would have marked a substantial departure from our long-standing approach – federal health programmes enacted to date make no pretence of mandating coverage.[5] To achieve the goal of universal coverage, however, President Clinton's plan had to go further. The Health Security Act of 1993 specifically stated that one of its purposes was 'to encourage all individuals to take responsibility for their health care coverage'.[6] To achieve this goal, the Clinton proposal actually would have created a dual set of requirements whose constitutionality was hotly debated internally: people in the US would have been told that they 'must enrol in an applicable health plan' and 'must pay any premium required'.[7] Although a variety of subsidies were provided, the ultimate responsibility for payment was with the individual. But the survival of the *status quo* – no universal system – reflects deep-seated opposition to government constraints being propounded in the interests of promoting health. Opponents to health reform capitalised upon public concerns about governmental intrusion in their lives, and this was in part responsible for the lack of political support for the Clinton reforms.

Such debates in the US barely scratch the surface of what governments may need to do to enforce health-promoting regulations. Individual behaviours (such as smoking, drug and alcohol abuse, high-calorie and high-fat diets, inadequate exercise, unsafe sex) are now major contributors to collective ill health, prompting calls for governmental constraints on individual freedom to engage in such behaviours. Leary notes that the International Covenant on Civil and Political Rights recognises that 'protection of public health is a permissible ground for limiting the rights to liberty of movement, freedom of religion, freedom of expression and the right to freedom of association'.[8]

With such a range of potential governmental interventions, real issues arise with respect to assessing the appropriate level of interference with individual rights. In an attempt to define a rational basis for evaluating the appropriate extent of government constraints on personal freedom, American legal scholar Larry Gostin and his colleagues have constructed a framework for assessing the propriety of governmental interference with individual rights in the public health context.[9] They begin by stating that the legitimacy of government action is always questionable when it involves control of human behaviours and approaches setting a moral agenda. After noting the origins of public health law in the inherent police power of the State, they believe that public health law is now being 'constitutionalised' to set limits on interference with individual rights. As a consequence, they propose that public health law should be reformed to focus on voluntary measures and would impose a stringent limit on the use of compulsory powers by requiring an individualised assessment that demonstrates a threat of significant risk. Whether Gostin's extensive procedural safeguards constitute the correct, or even a workable, approach, the proposal clearly illustrates the concerns raised by the trade-off between personal freedom and public health.

From my perspective, motorcycle helmet laws and other reasonable constraints on personal behaviour are well within the scope of proper government action. The consequences of allowing individuals to risk their brains at high speed are not merely threats to individual health, but also to the common well-being and public resources. The news story on Mr Busey went on to note that 'motorcycle accidents cause more than 4000 deaths and tens of thousands of brain injuries each year, and tax-payers pay most of the bills for hospitalization and continuing care ... According to a 1987 study of data from San Diego County, the average hospital cost for a motorcyclist injured while riding bareheaded is $42,291, as against $15,851 for one wearing a helmet'.[10] Our National Highway Traffic Safety Administration (NHTSA) just reported that deaths in automobile accidents in 1999 were the lowest for five years, there was a 10 per cent drop in pedestrian deaths and a drop in truck fatalities, but there was a rise in motorcycle fatalities from 1998 to 1999.[11]

Fortunately, even libertarians have a learning curve: Mr Busey is now reported not only to have recovered, but also to have found God and to have become an advocate for motorcycle helmet laws.

Similarly, I believe that the public interest served by governmental insistence that individuals participate in a national health coverage arrangement meets any balancing test against individual rights. The putatively voluntary coverage rules in the US sustain substantial social inequities behind a façade of free choice. On the one hand, we do have national health insurance for specific categories – for the postemployment generation, the most seriously disabled, and the kidney (for those suffering from end-stage renal disease) under Medicare, and for many low-income individuals under Medicaid.[12] The remaining 44-odd million uninsured people are left, literally, on their own to obtain care in community clinics and public hospitals and through private charity and philanthropy. But the 'uninsured' are not a fixed caste – rather, they constitute a category that encourages gaming and profiteering in the provision of health care coverage. Individuals become 'free riders', reaping the benefits of a health care delivery system largely paid for by others. Insurance companies collect premiums from healthy individuals, then withdraw from coverage once illness intervenes. Employers engage in elaborate schemes to avoid the health care costs of high-need individuals and their families. Public programmes that require one to demonstrate relative poverty through means-testing demonstrate vastly different 'take up' rates than do ones with universal eligibility rules, leaving many poor children uncovered who would be eligible. The social ethic of personal responsibility runs so deep that many individuals are averse to admitting that they cannot fulfil this responsibility and refuse to associate themselves and their families with being dependent on social programmes with a 'welfare stigma'.

Yet a society's collective health is in substantial part determined by the health care that can be obtained depending on one's wealth and insurance status. When a society views its responsibilities as merely on the margins, to establish measures dealing only with what are perceived to be the most dangerous public health threats and then only with the minimum level of intrusiveness necessary to accomplish that narrow purpose, the public health suffers, nominally in the name of protecting individual liberty. In the US, fostering a health care market-place has undermined, not enhanced, choice. Workers have limited options for coverage, and physicians have constraints not only on their financial arrangements but even on their medical judgements. The strongest protections of freedom are found not with respect to individual rights, but with respect to corporate interests – most employers can eliminate virtually any benefits they want to, and employers and their insurers alike are currently immunised against traditional liability law.[13] Moreover, while individual behaviours clearly affect population health, much illness and disability is random, genetically modulated, or otherwise not determined by individual choices. Human beings cannot choose illnesses and treatments as they do automobiles or cosmetics. In these circumstances, I believe that there is overwhelming justification for a legally established national coverage system.

But there is far more to the discussion of public health measures and rights than the consideration of personal liberty. Our collective health is the *ad hoc* result not only of how individuals choose to live and the health care that can be obtained, but also the social and physical environment we live in and the genetic profile we were born with.

Individual behaviour does not solely determine public health

Gostin's framework reflects the classic tension between public health and personal freedom. Although deeply concerned with governmental constraints on individual behaviour, Gostin, like others, notes that there are multiple sources of threats to the public's health. These can be conceptualised in three distinct, albeit overlapping, models: microbial, behavioural and ecological, each within the context of our once-immutable genetic substrate. Framing the issue as balancing public health with individual freedom fits well with the microbial and behavioural models of determinants of health, which have been the classical foci of public health laws and agencies, but less well with the ecological. The ecological model analyses illness, 'not as an external threat such as a pathogen or toxin, nor as a function of personal choices, but rather as a product of society's interaction with its environment'.[14] For example, smoking 'is not treated simply as a personal choice, but as a product of intense marketing efforts and a culture that fuels social attitudes and practices that promote the behavior'.[15] Governmental regulation with effective enforcement is often required. Flight attendants, for example, could not avoid cigarette smoke on their own; that required banning smoking on airplanes and enforcing the ban with medieval ferocity. Health insurance companies, driven by financial rather than communal health factors, will not on their own stop trying to insure only those whom they believe will not get sick. Children paralysed by random shootings made no conscious decision to put themselves in the path of bullets.

There is, then, need for an additional perspective beyond that of individual responsibility for public health. Moving beyond the individual level, however, raises many concerns and barriers. In this paper, two examples are presented to illustrate these concerns and barriers. First, interventions that address higher-order health determinants may implicate a panoply of rights in addition to personal freedom. The debate over the environmental impact of economic development highlights the new order of rights that emerge. Second, many of the measures that are required to moderate higher-order health determinants require international co-operation, which is far from easily accomplished. The current set of initiatives to deal with international commerce in hormone-stimulated beef and genetically modified agricultural products illustrates these complications, which emanate from deeply held nationalistic and cultural beliefs.

Environmental degradation, new-order rights and public health

A particular area in which governmental involvement to protect health has been pushed in recent years concerns economic development, which is seen as producing environmental and other risks to health when unfettered, and thus in need of tight regulation. This adverse relationship between economic development and health has been most prominently represented by the attention given to 'anthropogenic' climactic change i.e. global warming (a prominence generated for social, political, and rhetorical reasons, not simply scientific assessments, Jamieson notes[16]). There are, however, many other examples of global environmental change with health consequences, such as air and water pollution. The growing perception of the relationship between environmental change and health now means that 'the United States Environmental Protection Agency has become a public health agency'.[17]

It should be noted that concern for environmental and other ecological determinants of health has not mooted the importance of behavioural and microbial influences. Quite the contrary. Jamieson for one notes that 'it seems fairly certain that for the foreseeable future deaths caused by engaging in high-risk behaviors such as unprotected sex or smoking will continue to be much greater than the health risks posed by environmental change'.[18] Others have pointed out the increasing problem of emerging infectious diseases that now can spread rapidly with globalisation.[19] The point, then, is not that ecological factors are exclusive, rather that multiple influences on the public's health exist. In turn, governmental efforts to address each group of health determinants raises its own set of potential rights that can be affected.

Initiatives and procedures to cope with the health-related consequences of economic development have serious implications for rights that might be affected. Many have commented that a proper analysis of collective intervention to protect health in this context cannot be based on individual rights alone, but must extend to a broader range of rights. Juss states that 'in an increasingly fragile world environment, the emphasis on human rights must be on the ethical basis of our lives, rather than on individual rights *per se*'. This means going beyond rights that have been the traditional focus of concern, civil and political rights, to those that have been inadequately considered, economic, socio-cultural and solidarity rights.[20] To sustain human dignity 'as changes in our environment make dramatic inroads into the security of our lives,' Juss proposes a 'right of the individual and communities to live in stability with the unspoiled environment'.[21]

Based on considerations such as these, the larger ethical issue has largely been framed as the potential injustice of placing constraints on development for undeveloped societies, in order to protect the health of developed countries. This sets up the dilemma as one between developmental rights and rights to health. Juss, for example, having proposed a new set of environmentally related rights, observes nonetheless that 'a right to development ... is more likely to exist than a right to be unaffected by the unwelcome consequences of environmental degradation'.[22] This leads to a 'final question: do developing nations have a right to exploit the world's natural resources and thereby spoil the environment?"[23] The solution for Juss is to incorporate the environment into human rights thinking.

In short, global development is largely seen as degrading the environment in ways that will diminish health. Thus, measures to protect the public's health necessarily involve constraints on economic development. The cost of such measures can be great, thereby threatening economic growth in those societies most in need of development. The result is clearly a concern for the right to health of the developed world versus the right to development of the rest of the planet. This formulation raises a profound issue – should the potentially adverse health consequences of development justify the denial of economic advancement in much of the world? However critical this question may be, it does not go far enough in identifying the scope of the dilemma with respect to protecting health. It fails to take into account the positive relationship that is well established in the economic literature between economic status and health.[24] The relationship is particularly strong for very low versus high levels of income, precisely what is seen between undeveloped and developed societies. For at least the poorest nations, a relatively unfettered right to economic development at whatever cost to the environment may still have an overall net positive effect on health, both for the inhabitants of those countries and worldwide. Thus, the balance we need to strike is not simply between development and *adverse* health effects, but between development and *net* effects on health.

To summarise this perspective, the most basic statement of the issue before us has been that individual behaviour substantially determines individual health, which on a collective basis constitutes the public's health. To the extent that this paradigm holds, the trade-off is one between personal freedom and public health. It is clear, however, that individual behaviour is but one factor along with environmental and other ecological factors that determine individual health, and in turn, collective health. Thus, promoting public health requires actions that go beyond the individual level, such as environmental controls. While it is recognised that such interventions could affect rights other than just individual ones, much of the discussion has been within a framework in which economic development is largely seen as harming the environment in ways that diminish individual and collective health. Thus, a trade-off is recognised between the right to development and the right to health. But pitting health interests against developmental rights ignores the potentially positive contribution that economic development can have on the health of low-income populations. Taking this into account means that a proper focus should be on the net effects on health of respecting both individual (legal and political) rights as well as broader (economic, socio-cultural and solidarity) rights. In this limited context, the libertarian perspective may be well served.

This approach needs an upper limit: one cannot permit environmental degradation to reach a point at which continued growth in net health or even survival of humankind is threatened. Similarly, as the World Health Organisation has noted, 'while there is a close relationship between health and income at the very lowest income levels, as incomes begin to rise health hazards associated with economic development begin to emerge'.[25] Moreover, there is a time course to take into consideration: extremely short-term gains in health may not outweigh calamitous long-term environmental harm.

Addressing multiple health determinants implicates a new level of government intervention, with attendant difficulties of implementation

Whether the health threat emanates from global warming, hormone-stimulated beef, genetically modified agricultural products, radioactive emissions drifting in the atmosphere, or even ambient tobacco smoke, individual behaviour is no longer the only – or even a universally effective – target for protecting the public's health. Population health is not simply the sum of the consequences of individual choices made by members of the population. Many influences on health must now be addressed on a multinational basis, if at all.

Constructing interventions appropriate to a broad array of factors that influence health elevates the public health legal framework from the local police power, beyond the national constitutional power, to the international treaty level. It implicates not only individual rights, but also corporate rights and even national sovereignty. Protecting health in such a multifactorial context now becomes immediately intertwined with international commerce and international politics. It rapidly encounters barriers to acceptance and implementation, including highly divergent national interests and cultural attitudes toward science.

The modern global commercial world illustrates how far beyond the model of a single governmental body controlling individual behaviour through measures such as mandatory motorcycle helmet laws one might need to go to protect public health. Just as the EPA in the United States may been seen as a public health agency, the World Trade Organisation (WTO) 'appears to fast becoming (*sic*) the "world trans-science organization"'.[26] In that capacity, the WTO now deals with the scientific and technical issues concerning health issues such as feed additive antibiotics or hormone-stimulated beef. The WTO approach to health issues highlights both the transnational character of the governmental intervention required and the widely divergent interests that can be affected by such intervention. In particular, it illuminates the need to consider the different perspectives and interests of (would-be) developing and developed populations.

Under the rules of the WTO's Agreement on Technical Barriers to Trade, for example, to challenge a signatory country's regulations that restrict imports which it fears could affect public health and safety, a would-be exporting country has the burden of proving the controls are more restrictive than necessary.[27] While the United States marshalled and presented scientific evidence sufficient to enable American beef-exporting interests to prevail on the hormone-treatment debate, developing countries may not have the resources to challenge restrictive regulations. Nor may they be able to meet standards they cannot challenge: 'While developed countries seek integration of environmental concerns into trade rules ... the developing world opposes this effort on the ground that it will effectively impose unattainable environmental standards, thus preventing goods from poorer countries from entering the world market.'[28]

Another relevant factor is greatly differing opinions over the standards that should be used for determining what is and what is not good for the health of oneself and one's neighbours, let alone one's country or continent or planet. The public does not easily vest the authority to set such standards in the hands of scientists or regulators. Both individual beliefs and commercial interests tightly constrain action by government, even action urged by the recognised scientific establishment.

A recent brouhaha in the US over health claims that can be made on behalf of so-called dietary supplements exemplifies this interaction between scientific evidence and individual or commercial preferences. In response to tremendous public and industry reaction to its proposed rules that would have seriously restricted health claims for dietary supplements, the federal Food and Drug Administration eased those restrictions. At issue is not whether the products can be sold, and whether people can follow their own preferences by purchasing them, but only what claims can be made without prior scientific review by the agency. According to an article in *The Inquirer* (Philadelphia) of 6 January 2000, under the new rules 'the products can legally claim to treat various symptoms – from morning sickness to memory loss – that are considered common passages of life ... At issue are the $6 billion worth of dietary supplements that Americans buy each year – pills, capsules and teas that do not undergo any government scrutiny for safety or effectiveness before being sold ... That means supplements could claim to ease ordinary morning sickness, but not toxemia or other serious pregnancy complications'.

The American struggle to balance science and popular beliefs concerning dietary supplements echoes the current fight over genetically altered foodstuffs in Europe, and particularly in the United Kingdom. In an article entitled 'The Pharmageddon Riddle', Michael Specter, a correspondent for *The New Yorker* who is based in Rome, chronicled the tumultuous course that the Monsanto Corporation has encountered in its push to promote biotechnology in agriculture.[29] Monsanto's stated goal in focusing on biotechnology seems laudable: to help people 'lead longer, healthier lives, at costs that they and their nations can afford and without continued environmental degradation'. Yet they face staunch opposition from many quarters, including nobility such as the Prince of Wales himself and Lord Peter Melchett. Instead of the saviours of mankind, Monsanto is 'seen as a symbol of corporate imperialism' and stands accused of manipulating nature to create 'frankenfoods'.

Public resistance to government actions – such as in the US over dietary supplements and in Europe over genetically altered foodstuffs – comes in large part when government proposes to require compliance with scientific evidence on what's good for the health of individuals or the population. People don't mistrust science as such; they simply want to make choices among the variety of purportedly healthful activities on their own – and often to balance those choices against their own ability to earn a living. Specific regulatory actions are judged not only on their individual merits, but also on their potential to signal expanding governmental encroachment on individual and commercial behaviours. Hence, we have a continuing struggle between those who believe they know what is healthful and those who want to be left alone. Specter quotes Lord Melchett as saying that 'People do things for all sorts of reasons that are rational, but they are not scientific or technical … If it's acceptable to choose your car based on emotion and not science, why should it be wrong to choose your food that way?' The chairman and CEO of biotechnology giant Novartis explained their decision to stop using genetically modified ingredients in Gerber baby foods by saying: 'This is not just about plants. It's about our myths, our history and culture … How could something this important *not* scare people?'[30]

Since I'm from Chicago, I will cite our infamous former resident, Mr Al Capone, as a final example of the problems with popular resistance to government deciding what is good for people. Because of our federalist structure and the reservation of police power to the states, it took an amendment to our Constitution, not simply an Act of Congress, to ban intoxicating liquors throughout the United States. This was the most formal nationwide public health measure in our history, and it was a disaster. For the nearly 15 years that the Eighteenth Amendment was in effect, illegal and highly unhealthful individual and commercial behaviour ran amok in the United States. Mr Capone capitalised – literally – on the seemingly indomitable insistence of the American people to express their freedom to pickle their own livers. We have had a parallel situation for many years with respect to marijuana, cocaine and heroin.

What are the lessons from these experiences? First, the locus of governmental authority may determine whether measures necessary to protect health are possible. Just as the states in the US retain the 'police power' and the federal government cannot impose certain constraints on individual behaviour, sovereign nations may not cede to multinational bodies the authority needed to take transnational actions to protect health. Second, cultural, religious or other beliefs – including the desire to be free to engage in entrepreneurial activities – may trump science in the public's mind. However rational proposed constraints on personal freedom or other rights may be, they may be ineffective if they run counter to popular notions of what is healthful or reach the limits of tolerable constraints on even unhealthful activities.

A framework for assessing governmental interventions across a broad array of health determinants

Developing and implementing a workable approach to governmental involvement in promoting health at many different levels, from the national to the global, would require a substantial number of steps. One complex task would be to develop and put into place a 'net effects' balancing formula. Another would be establishing procedures to assure consideration of widely divergent attitudes toward science and health. There would need to be mechanisms to enforce the results. Finally, the potentially catastrophic consequences of miscalculating 'net effects' would require continued oversight through direct evaluation and related research to forestall passing any fail-safe point.

Interventions in this expanded framework require an analytical framework that, unlike Gostin's, balances the free exercise of a range of rights against the net health production. It must take into account, for example, that a 'threat of significant risk' to public health from the establishment of an environmentally harmful enterprise would be weighed differently in different contexts. In a developed country the net effect on health is likely to be negative, since the direct adverse effect on health would be measurable while the marginal increase in wealth would have only a small positive effect, if any, on health. But in a developing country, the net effect on health might well be positive if the marginal impact on wealth were great. In a global context, the overall net effect would have to weigh the enhancement of health in the developing country as well as the diminution in health in the wealthy country.

Such a far-reaching approach to governmental interventions would need to accommodate vastly disparate views on science and health, as well as competing interests such as global commerce. This would not be accomplished easily. Even on the level of individual behaviour, reaching consensus on appropriate controls proves to be an imposing challenge. Deaths from motor vehicle injuries, homicide, suicide and HIV-related infections have all been on the same order of magnitude in recent years in the United States, and lag far behind tobacco-related deaths. Yet the threshold for societal intervention and the character of acceptable interventions vary greatly among those causes of mortality, for reasons other than scientific ones.

Establishing enforcement mechanisms would have to overcome many barriers. Should environmental protection and health be a predominant concern of the World Trade Organisation, as some would insist? Or, should the World Health Organisation be able to trump the World Trade Organisation? Should any transnational organisation have such powers? The American perspective and legal context reflects our inherently laissez-faire, market-oriented social compact, which permits and sustains a wide range of activities and behaviours without health-based constraints. The result is disparate health status and health care access. Remedying this is all the more difficult because of the decentralised, federalist structure of our government, which reflects deep distrust of strong central government. This attitude is mirrored across the world in governmental approaches toward international co-operation that involves any potential diminution of national sovereignty.

Finally, this is a high-risk enterprise. The potentially catastrophic consequences of miscalculating what should and should not be permitted include threatening the global food supply or irreversibly altering the environment to make it lethal to mankind. If such a comprehensive approach to protecting health is to be undertaken, it should in fact protect, not destroy, health. This would require continued research and oversight to forestall passing any fail-safe point.

References

1. Epstein R A. *Mortal peril: our inalienable right to health care?* Addison Wesley, 1997; *see also* Brennan T A. Moral imperatives versus market solutions: is health care a right? *U. Chi. L. Rev.* 1998; 65: 345–63.
2. *Ibid.*
3. Hinds M de C. Consumer's world; bareheaded motorcyclists pressed anew to cover up. *New York Times* 1989; 14 January: 50.
4. *Ibid.*
5. Medicaid is a voluntary program that states must decide to participate in before any individual has the federal entitlement to coverage that it provides. Medicare creates a direct entitlement in individuals, and a mandatory payroll tax, but the statute has no requirement that senior citizens participate.
6. Proposed legislation: 'The Health Security Act of 1993'. United States House of Representatives. Doc. Number 103–174. Washington: US Government Printing Office, 1993, §3 (6), at 7.
7. *Ibid.*, §1002(a).
8. Leary V A. The right to health in international human rights law. *Health Hum. Rights* 1994; 1 (1): 24–56.
9. Gostin L O, Buris S, Lazzarini S. The law and the public's health: a study of infectious disease law in the United States. *Columbia Law Review* 1999; 99: 59–128.
10. Hinds, *Op. cit.*
11. Quoted in *American Healthline* (Bowles, 4/4).
12. Social Security Act, Title XVIII (Medicare, including the End Stage Renal Disease Program) and Title XIX (Medicaid).
13. Rosenblatt R E, Law S A, Rosenbaum S. *Law and the American health care system.* Westbury, NY: The Foundation Press Inc., 1997, chapter 2, §§ C–E, chapter 3, §I.
14. Gostin, *Op. cit.*, at 74.
15. *Ibid.*, at 75.
16. Jamieson D. Global responsibilities: ethics, public health, and global environmental change. *Indiana Journal of Global Legal Studies* 1997; 5: 99–119.
17. *Ibid.*, at 105.
18. Jamieson, *Op. cit.*, 114.
19. Howson C P, Fineberg H V, Bloom B R. The pursuit of global health: the relevance of engagement for developed countries. *Lancet* 1998; 351 (9102): 586–90; Fidler D P. The globalization of public health: emerging infectious diseases and international relations. *Ind. J. Global Leg. Stud.* 1997; 5: 11–51.
20. Juss S. Global environmental change: health and the challenge for human rights. *Ind. J. Global Leg. Stud.* 1997; 5: 121–78.
21. *Ibid.*, at 122.
22. *Ibid.*, at 123.
23. *Ibid.*
24. Feinstein J S. The relationship between socioeconomic status and health: a review of the literature. *Milbank Quarterly* 1993; 71: 279–322.

25. World Health Organisation. Global strategy for health for all by the year 2000. Geneva: WHO. As quoted in Leary, *Op. cit.*

26. Weinberg M S. *International perspectives: service providers; technical barriers to trade (non-tariff measures)*. Metropolitan Corporate Counsel; 1999: 48.

27. *Ibid.*

28. Gutermann P E, Reifschneider L M. Environmental issues affect global trade talks. *National Law Journal* 1999; 22 November; B11.

29. Specter M. The Pharmageddon Riddle. *The New Yorker* 2000; 10 April: 58–71.

30. *Ibid.*

Chapter 8

Culture, conformity and mental health (1)

Jonathan Glover

There was a report recently of a woman who had spent much of her life in a psychiatric hospital, having been admitted back in the 1950s because she was an unmarried mother. In that period being gay was also counted as a qualification for psychiatric treatment. We now think of that period as the dark ages: how *can* people have thought that single parenthood or being gay were signs of psychiatric disorder? These are reminders of the importance of not defining 'mental health' in terms of cultural conformity. The whole tradition of thinking of mental illness in terms of 'deviance' has something deeply wrong with it, wrapping up the pressure to conform in medical jargon.

The reaction to that kind of psychiatry was the anti-psychiatry movement of the 1960s, which challenged the whole idea of psychiatric illness. That movement had its well-known excesses. There was the unsubstantiated claim that schizophrenia was caused by the person's family. There were some of R D Laing's comments, such as that in the future people will see those with schizophrenia as Renaissance explorers and their condition as 'one of the forms in which … the light began to break through the cracks in our all-too-closed minds'.[1] Modern psychiatrists tend to look back with distaste on both the cultural conformity of 1950s practice and on the wild statements of the 1960s psychiatric cultural revolution. Both have been replaced by the patient empirical unravelling of the causes, especially the biological ones, of particular psychiatric conditions, and by the development of less dogmatic kinds of psychotherapy and of more fine tuned kinds of medication.

But there are some things that deserve to be rescued from the anti-psychiatry movement, and one is concerned with the conceptual boundaries of psychiatric illness. If the word 'illness' applies, the psychological condition must involve something more substantial than deviation from cultural norms. It must involve some kind of psychological malfunctioning. In the case of schizophrenia, it is not hard to show that, far from being a state in which the light breaks on Renaissance explorers, it is a condition involving substantial cognitive deficits and distortions. Kay Redfield Jamison's fine books, in which a scientific concern for evidence is combined with powerful description from the inside, bring out the way in which manic depression involves emotional states that are distressing – often to the point of inducing suicide – and massively incapacitating. In these cases the medical model is not wrong: psychological systems are malfunctioning in ways that reduce people's capacities, distort their understanding or cause them great distress.

It is important to separate the cognitive and emotional states that are indicative of psychological disorder from others which have a different causal history. 'Delusions' are sometimes defined as beliefs persisted in despite their failure to correspond to reality. An atheist may consider religious beliefs both to be false and to be often held with great persistence, despite arguments against them being presented. A believer in one religion may take a similar view of the beliefs of a rival religion. But psychiatrists confronted with people who hold religious beliefs they do not themselves share do not automatically suggest a course of treatment for these 'delusions'. Even if a particular set of religious beliefs is considered to be false, the prevalence of such beliefs in the culture allows alternative explanations of why an individual may hold them without postulating some cognitive impairment. Similarly, a person's state of great emotional distress after being bereaved need not be a sign of any psychological malfunctioning. Nor was the distress caused to many gay people by the prejudices of the 1950s.

Personality disorders

If the concept of mental illness is to be defensible, there has to be psychological malfunctioning. Without this, there is nothing to be 'treated' and so nothing for the 'medical model' to apply to. And the 'malfunctioning' has to be specifiable in terms other than mere cultural non-conformity. Minority sexual preferences, or minority lifestyle preferences, are not in themselves signs of mental illness.

It is not hard to defend the application of the medical model to schizophrenia and manic depression. But it is much less clear that some other conditions which bring people to the attention of psychiatrists are appropriately thought of in medical terms. This applies notably to some of the so-called 'personality disorders'.

The term 'personality disorder' is usually defined in terms of 'deeply ingrained maladaptive patterns of behaviour, resulting in distress to self or others'. Within this category the classification of particular personality disorders varies, but there are some diagnostic categories that appear in most lists. Histrionic or Hysterical Personality Disorder and Narcissistic Personality Disorder involve having roughly the kinds of personality the names suggest. So does Paranoid Personality Disorder.

Schizoid Personality Disorder is often described in terms of a defective capacity for relationships, a lack of empathy, and being cold, detached, withdrawn and solitary. Obsessive–Compulsive Personality Disorder is said to be characterised by rigidity, conformity, excessive conscientiousness, perfectionism, and by being stingy with both money and emotions.

In the definition of 'personality disorder', the worrying word is 'maladaptive'. Conformity is in many environments much more 'adaptive' than non-conformity. What is maladaptive depends on the local culture. In the 1950s, to be gay or to be communist was extremely maladaptive in our local culture. And Socrates' persistent questioning and argument was obviously a deeply ingrained pattern of behaviour that turned out to be highly maladaptive.

The fact that psychiatric definitions are sometimes easy to pull apart need not indicate a very deep flaw. Medical disciplines are to some extent crafts, learned in practice rather than out of books. Psychiatrists may develop a practical understanding of things going wrong in people which is not always adequately reflected in textbook definitions.

In practice there seem to be two different models influencing thought about personality disorders. One comes from psychiatry and one from psychology. The psychiatric model is rooted in the idea of a kind of personality that is prone to a particular kind of psychiatric breakdown. Schizoid Personality Disorder can be seen as a possible precursor state for schizophrenia. The psychological model is based on the conception of dimensions of personality: the idea, for instance, that we all come somewhere on the continuum of extraversion and introversion. On this model, those with personality disorders are at an extreme end of a continuum: the person with Schizoid Personality Disorder perhaps being an extreme introvert.

Neither of these models seems adequate to establish that personality disorders should be seen as psychiatric illnesses. The psychiatric model seems to confuse liability to illness with illness itself. Some kinds of people are more prone than others to heart attacks, but this does not show that *being that kind of person* is itself an illness. And the psychological model does equally badly. There is nothing in itself harmful or incapacitating about being at an extreme on some dimension. There is the suspicion that cultural conformity is the criterion lurking behind this conception of personality disorder.

One way of trying to avoid this suspicion could be to appeal to an Aristotelian idea of the good life for people, rooted in a conception of human nature. It is plausible that the good life is a species-related concept. Caging a bird is an outrage, and one reason for thinking this is that it is in the nature of birds to fly and preventing this may cause them great frustration. Keeping a human being for a long period in solitary confinement is an outrage, and one reason for this may be the Aristotelian one that by nature man is a social animal, so that enforced solitariness is extremely cruel. This idea of a species-specific good life for human beings could be applied to Schizoid Personality Disorder. If sociability is part of that good life, then those who fear or dislike sociability could be said to have personalities that intrinsically reduce their quality of life, thus making psychiatric treatment appropriate.

There is something to be said for the Aristotelian approach to psychiatry. But it has its dangers. Take Obsessive–Compulsive Personality Disorder. If you are my psychiatrist and give me this diagnosis, I may challenge you about it. Why do you say this stigmatising thing about my personality? You may say that I have the appropriate symptoms: rigidity, conformity, excessive conscientiousness and perfectionism, as well as being stingy with money and with my emotions. But I may reply that where you think me too rigid and conscientious, I see you as so flexible and pragmatic as to be sloppy and unprincipled. I think my financial prudence compares well with your spendthrift approach to life. And, as for the charge that I am stingy with my emotions, I find my reticence more dignified that your tearful, touchy-feely willingness to make an exhibition of yourself.

Clearly people have different personal styles and one worry is that those who write the 'personality disorder' chapters in psychiatric textbooks are medicalising styles they do not feel comfortable with. There is a parlour game we can all play of diagnosing the personality disorder that best fits each of our friends. The philosopher needed here as a corrective to Aristotle is John Stuart Mill, for one danger of the idea of personality disorder is its possible use against human variety, to stifle what Mill called 'experiments in living'.

We should not be too quick to accept that 'personality disorders' are a medical problem. But this does not mean that psychiatrists have to steer clear of them. Sometimes people feel they would like to be different from the way they are, and psychiatric techniques – whether psychotherapy or pharmacology – may be helpful to them. Even in cases of relatively uncontroversial psychiatric illness, the boundary between features of the illness and features of the person's own personality may be a blurred one.

Some psychiatrists who prescribe Prozac are troubled by this. When Prozac is used to treat someone's depression, its effects may go beyond this to changing the person's personality: improving self-esteem, reducing an excessive sensitivity to conflict and to the needs of others. It is always possible to say that the Prozac is prescribed on a continuing basis to ward off any future recurrence of depression. But some reflective psychiatrists, Peter Kramer for instance, who discusses this issue in his *Listening to Prozac*, are aware of being influenced by the view that the person is better off because of the change in underlying personality. It is worrying, because the psychiatrist is moving out of the medical role. But perhaps this does not matter so long as there is honesty about this and the decision is firmly in the hands of the person whose personality it is, rather than in those of the psychiatrist. The central ethical points here are about autonomy and informed consent.

Antisocial Personality Disorder

The most contentious category of all is Antisocial Personality Disorder, or what the law calls 'psychopathic personality'. People with this condition show a persistent pattern of irresponsible and antisocial behaviour. They are said to lack control over their impulses, to be bad at long-term planning, and to be frequent liars. They are also often said to 'lack a conscience'.

One question is about whether this condition is treatable. Psychiatrists are divided about this, some saying that certain kinds of therapy are helpful, others saying that no properly substantiated 'cure' exists.

Another question about those with this condition is whether they should be thought of as victims of a profound psychiatric disturbance, or whether they are just particularly nasty and amoral people. When someone is called a psychopath, is this an excuse because he or she has 'something missing', or is it a particularly severe moral condemnation?

I doubt if we will resolve this question until we have more understanding of psychopaths from the inside. For instance, what does their 'lack of conscience' come to? There are various things that could be meant by this. They may lack empathy: perhaps they have little idea of how other people feel when treated with brutality or cruelty. Or perhaps it is sympathy they lack: they do know how others feel, but don't care. Or perhaps they lack feelings of guilt or remorse, the normal emotional responses linked to the thought of having done something wrong. Or it may be moral concepts that are missing: perhaps they have little grasp of what it means to say that something is selfish, cruel or unfair? Or is it that they lack a conception of the sort of person they are, or a picture of the sort of person they want to be, together with the values that shape that picture? This is one of the areas of psychiatry where biological and sociological studies of causes need to be supplemented by a more humanistic approach: seeking an understanding from the inside by asking them questions about how they see things and especially how they see themselves.

Whatever it is that those with Antisocial Personality Disorder lack, it is fairly clear that a high proportion of them have had desperately sad childhoods. Many of them suffered child abuse; many were removed from their families and sent to children's homes; few of them felt wanted or were nourished by love. The deep question this raises is how far such a history counts as an excuse, how far it should mitigate the moral revulsion against them that we feel when hearing of the horrendous crimes they have sometimes committed. Sometimes knowing more about the story of their lives can create a tension: the crimes remain unforgivable enormities, but knowing the whole history can make the perpetrators seem victims too.

Let me illustrate this with one case history: a real case, not an invented one. It concerns someone I will call 'Mr H'. He had a notably unhappy childhood. His father was strict, a man with a terrible temper, who was a 'demon' about punctuality. He insisted on silence in the family. The children never dared to speak in his presence unless spoken to, and were not allowed to call him anything less formal than 'Father'. When he wanted his son, he never called him by name, but always whistled for him in the way he called for his dog. The father often beat the dog, his wife and each of his children. As a child, Mr H was once given 230 strokes of the cane by his father. In later life, he remembered, or thought he remembered, seeing his drunk father rape his mother.

Mr H grew up with a very rigid personality. As an adult he was obsessed with cleanliness, passionately hating any untidiness or dirt. He was also obsessed with wolves, sometimes thinking of himself as a wolf, and called his Alsatian dog 'Wolf'. He took the dog for exactly the same walk every day, throwing a stick for it at exactly the same place. Any suggestion of varying such routines made him agitated and angry. He hated being left alone at night, and hated the moon because he thought it was dead. He was obsessed with his own possible death from cancer, the cause of his mother's death.

Mr H had difficulties in his love life. As a boy he had been terrified of being kissed. His first love affair came when he was 37. It was with a teenage girl, who tried to kill herself when he abruptly broke off the relationship. He then fell in love with his niece, who did not reciprocate his feelings. She killed herself with his pistol. At the age of 41, he had another affair, this time with an 18-year-old girl, who made an unsuccessful suicide attempt early in their relationship. Mr H seems to have been disgusted by normal sexual intercourse, saying it would make him 'infected'. His niece said his main sexual pleasure was in getting her to urinate on his face.

Much of his emotional life seems to have been diverted to patriotism and politics. He fought in a war, with great patriotic enthusiasm. He was temporarily blinded during a gas attack, which left him with great resentment against those who did not fight in the war. He took up extreme right-wing politics and was passionately anti-Semitic. He was highly successful at appealing to the public. He became leader of his country. He started a world war. He ordered the systematic murder of millions of his fellow citizens. He killed himself when his country lost the war.

Now that Mr H's identity has emerged, it will be clear that he was never formally diagnosed as having Antisocial Personality Disorder. But, apart from details, his history differs only in scale from many who have that diagnosis. And that history puts in dramatic form the moral challenge to those who hope to understand the disorder. The challenge is to combine an undiminished revulsion at the atrocities perpetrated in one perspective with the thought that, given such a childhood, many of us might have turned out not so very different.

Dangerousness and civil liberties

Let us hope that none of those now diagnosed as having Antisocial Personality Disorder will have the chance to do as much harm as Mr H. But, on a less world historic scale, some of them are very dangerous. How should society respond to the dangers they present?

The present UK Home Secretary has put forward proposals for compulsory detention, in the interests of protecting the public, of those who are diagnosed as having Severe Antisocial Personality Disorder, and who are also predicted by psychiatrists to be dangerous. In the debate over this proposal, very important values are at stake on both sides. On the one hand, there is an obvious breach of civil liberties. Most of us prefer to live in a society where being locked up results from being convicted in court of a crime, rather than from the fact that someone predicts we are likely to commit a crime. On the other hand, as the Home Secretary has pointed out, our civil liberties also include not being attacked, raped or murdered.

The principle that people should not be deprived of liberty unless they have been convicted in a court of a crime is central to our civil liberties. But there are what are generally held (rightly, I believe) to be justifiable exceptions. There is the power of the police to detain someone for questioning, acceptable only because there is a clear time limit to this power. There is the power of a court to remand someone in custody, acceptable because it applies only pending a trial. There are more serious exceptions than these temporary ones. There is the possibility (recognised in the European Convention on Human Rights) of compulsorily detaining someone to prevent the spread of a serious infectious disease. And there are the powers to 'section' someone, to detain them in a psychiatric hospital, under one or other section of the Mental Health Act.

The Mental Health Act allows the detention of people in hospital under certain conditions. They have to have a mental disorder (section 3 of the 1983 Act specifically includes 'psychopathic disorder'). But simply having a mental disorder is not enough: the detention has to be either in the interests of their own health or safety or else intended to protect others. And there is a further condition: the detention has to be necessary for treatment (defined in terms of either alleviating the disorder or stopping it from deteriorating). This last condition – the 'treatability test' – is the central feature that marks off the present law from the new proposals. Without the treatability test, the present law would provide what the Government hopes for. It would allow people to be detained because of their psychopathic disorder, where this was intended for the protection of others. But, since the psychiatric profession is divided over whether 'psychopathic disorder' is treatable, the treatability test blocks the detention of some possibly dangerous people with this condition.

To many, it seems obvious that dropping the treatability test is justified. Those who support the new proposals think that the predictions of dangerousness would be right about two-thirds of the time. The suggestion is that, in a year, 300 people might be detained under the proposals. Of those 300, 100 would not in fact have committed violent offences and 200 would have done so. Saving 200 people from being assaulted, in some cases from being raped or killed, is not trivial.

But there are serious worries on the other side. One is about the 100 people detained who would not in fact have done the kind of thing predicted. Is this margin of error acceptable when people's liberties are at stake?

But the more fundamental worry concerns the implications of dropping the treatability test. That test means detention under the current Mental Health Act has a justification to do with the medical interests of the patient. Abandoning this requirement turns the issue into one of preventive detention. The psychiatrist who has no treatment to offer these patients will have with them the relationship not of a doctor but of a jailer.

Once the matter becomes no longer a medical issue, but one of preventive detention, an alarming slippery slope looms. If we allow this group of people to be detained because of predictions that they are dangerous, what about other groups? There are people with AIDS who might be predicted to have unprotected sex. There are people with political views that might justify predictions that they are potential terrorist bombers or potential racist arsonists. To allow people to be locked up on the basis of merely predicted rather than actual crimes has implications frightening to those of us who care about civil liberties.

There are two qualifications to this. One is that there is the special case of predictions based on a person's expressed intentions; the other is a hypothetical case where the prediction is virtually a certainty.

Some people with HIV or AIDS say they will get revenge for what has happened to them by passing it on to as many other people as possible. In this kind of case it seems hugely costly in lives to wait until someone can be shown to have been given HIV by that person. In such a case I would support preventive detention where necessary. There are two grounds for this. One is the general exception allowed under the European Convention where detention is necessary to prevent the spread of serious infectious disease. The other is that by expressing this intention, the person may be held to have opted into the system of social restraint – he or she has lost the entitlement to the presumption of being harmless.

The other qualification rests on the kind of thought experiment that philosophers love and which most other people find infuriating. In the case of Antisocial Personality Disorder, the predictions of dangerousness are far from total reliability. But suppose we had predictions (perhaps based on some brain scan technique that is now only science fiction) that were 100 per cent reliable? Surely it would then be only an extraordinarily doctrinaire civil libertarian who would insist that we had to wait until *after* a rape or murder had happened, rather than preventing it by prior restraint? I agree that this would be absurd. There is of course a huge difference between this hypothetical case and the actual position, so that conceding this hypothetical point does not entail support for the current proposals.

But conceding the point is of some theoretical importance. Civil liberties can be thought of in two ways. They can be thought of as absolute rights or as *prima facie* rights. An absolute right is one that in all circumstances trumps all other considerations. I am always wary of absolute rights, as it is hard to predict what disasters may prove unavoidable because we have boxed ourselves in by making some right utterly inviolable. And, in the case of not being detained unless convicted of a crime, this is an implausible absolute right. It would mean, in the hypothetical case considered, waiting until the absolutely inevitable murder took place before intervening, rather than preventing it. It would also mean not detaining the carrier of the deadly disease, no matter how great the catastrophe of the resulting epidemic. Some libertarians may go to these heroic lengths, but we should think a long time before following them.

What then happens to the civil liberties position? For those of us who do not believe in the absolute right, but who still care about civil liberties, the best approach seems to be to say that this is still a right, not an absolute one but one that can be overridden only as a last resort to prevent a great disaster. What does this come to in practice? Since someone being killed is a great disaster, does this mean that the civil liberty becomes vacuous and is easily trumped by the case for the Government's preventive detention policy?

Part of the answer to this is to be found in the phrase 'as a last resort'. When it is proposed to gain a benefit or avoid an evil by overriding civil liberties, the question should always be asked whether there is a way of achieving as beneficial a result by means less costly to liberty. The predicted benefit from the proposed preventive detention policy is that, of the 57,000 violent crimes each year, 200 will be prevented. This is a small proportion, but of some importance if you happen to be one of the 200 victims, a few of whom will be killed and many of whom will be injured.

The question to ask is, are there methods by which such a reduction in death and injury could be brought about at less cost to liberty? To this the answer is certainly 'Yes'. Every year, 5000 children are killed or seriously injured by cars. Recently, the Government refused to reduce the general urban speed limit from 30 mph to 20 mph, which is roughly the limit more common in other European countries. At 30 mph, nearly half the children hit by cars are killed. At 20 mph, only 5 per cent are killed. A 20 mph speed limit would avoid far more death and injury than the Government's psychiatric proposals. Of course, a reduction in the speed limit reduces the freedom of car drivers, but this hardly compares with the erosion of the central civil liberty involved in preventive detention based on psychiatric prediction.

Those who think the civil liberty in question is an absolute will, of course, oppose the preventive detention proposals. But even those of us who are wary of such absolutes have good reason to resist them. They fail even the weaker 'last resort' test: there being no alternative less morally costly way of bringing about an equivalent benefit.

Part of the moral cost of the proposals would be borne by those who would lose their liberty under them. But the other moral cost to bear in mind is the possible extension of the principle of preventive detention to other groups who might be thought dangerous. It would be less worrying if there were some clear and defensible principle that explained why *this* group of dangerous people should be singled out, a principle which would give some security against further erosion of civil liberties. At the meeting when the government proposals were launched, I asked the Home Secretary on what principle these dangerous people, rather than others, were singled out. His reply was that these people were different because of their sudden and unpredictable violence. No doubt there is truth in this description of psychopathic violence. But a future administration might take the view that predictable assaults and murders based on carefully thought out plans were just as bad as unpredictable ones. The reply was not entirely reassuring.

I do not want to pretend that rejecting the preventive detention proposals has no cost. Serious moral and political decisions often require choosing between different values, both of which have a real claim on us. The defence of civil liberties is not cost-free. And those whose liberties are at stake are not a particularly popular group. But one way of judging a society is by how far it protects the liberties of unattractive, unpopular groups of people. Whether or not we care about the liberties even of such people says something about the sort of people we are. And in this case it may in the long term make a real difference to the sort of society we end up living in.

References

1.   Laing R D. *The politics of experience*. Harmondsworth: Penguin Books, 1967: 107

Chapter 9

Culture, conformity and mental health (2)

Kay Redfield Jamison

I am delighted to have the opportunity to talk about culture, conformity and mental health. I can, of course, address only a few issues related to this very broad subject, and even those rather glancingly. I am a scientist and a clinician, but I am also someone who suffers from a severe mental illness – manic depression. My remarks will reflect these different perspectives.

I would like to focus on two topics: first suicide; and, second the thin line that sometimes separates those with mental illness from those of great accomplishment in the arts and sciences. Both topics have critical implications for society: suicide, because it is often preventable and always so devastating in its impact on those left behind; and, the permeable boundaries between madness and creativity, because this very permeability raises ethical issues that capture the promise, and the difficulties, inherent to genetic research.

These topics also exemplify the problems brought about by the quite striking lack of substantive public education about mental illness and science. We have romanticised mental illness; we have stigmatised mental illness; we have trivialised it; and we have marginalised it. But we have not taught the public what we do know about the symptoms, treatments and causes of psychiatric disorders.

The illnesses I will be focusing on here – depression and manic depression (or, bipolar disorder) – are common. One person in six during his or her lifetime will suffer from clinical depression, and one in a hundred from manic depression. These mood disorders are painful, closely tied to alcohol and drug abuse, potentially lethal, not infrequently result in violence, and they are economically costly. They are also among the most treatable conditions in medicine. Fortunately, the science underlying the most severe mental illnesses is progressing rapidly. Geneticists are actively searching for the genes for schizophrenia, manic-depressive illness and other psychiatric disorders; neuroscientists are mapping the regions in the brain most implicated in psychopathology; and psychopharmacologists and psychotherapists are developing better and more specific treatments.

But, still, there is a terrible gap between what we know and what we do. And few of us are adequately prepared to grapple with the immense ethical issues that will arise from the research in neuroscience.

The first topic I would like to address, that of suicide, reflects more than any I know, the deadly gap between what we know about a public health problem and what we do about it, between what psychiatric science knows and what the public knows. And, in fact, we know a great deal about suicide.

We know, first, that it is a terrible killer: in the United States, suicide is the third major cause of death in 15–19 year olds, and it is the second leading cause of death in college students. In 1996, more teenagers and young adults died from suicide than from cancer, heart disease, AIDS, stroke, diabetes and lung disease *combined*. It kills the young dreadfully and disproportionately. And, across the world, in those between the ages of 15 and 44, suicide is the second leading killer of women and the fourth of men.

In addition to actual suicide, studies conducted by the Centers for Disease Control and Prevention in Atlanta find that one in ten college students and one in five high school students state having seriously considered committing suicide in the preceding year. Nearly one high school student in ten stated that he or she had actually attempted suicide. Each year in the United States there are more than 500,000 suicide attempts serious enough to warrant medical treatment in an emergency room.

We understand – up to a point – the mental states of those who kill themselves: the despair, depression, irritability, agitation and the sheer hopelessness. And we have learned a great deal from suicide notes, suicide diaries, psychological autopsies and clinical interviews with people who have survived very severe suicide attempts.

We have compelling evidence that the single most important factor in suicide is psychopathology. The major psychiatric and addictive illnesses – depression, manic depression, schizophrenia, alcohol and drug abuse, severe anxiety disorders, and borderline and antisocial personality disorders – are involved in more than 90 per cent of all suicides. Combining depression and alcohol or drug abuse is especially lethal. Clearly, most people who are depressed will not kill themselves. But of those who kill themselves, the majority are profoundly depressed.

We also know a great deal, although not nearly enough, about the underlying biology of suicide: for example, that there is a component which is probably independent of – but interacts dangerously with – the genetic factors implicated in the major psychiatric illnesses. And we know that certain neurotransmitters such as serotonin, norepinephrine and dopamine are deeply enmeshed in the volatility, impetuousness and violence that are part and parcel of the moody and explosive temperaments most closely associated with self-murder. And violence *is*, unquestionably, an integral part of many suicides. The igniting of a volatile temperament by a psychological stress, or by the presence of a depressive illness or other psychiatric disorder, is often deadly.

We are fortunate to have very effective ways to treat the psychiatric illnesses most commonly associated with suicide. We have a wide variety of antidepressant medications and therapies: lithium, anticonvulsant medications, psychotherapy, drugs to treat anxiety, and drugs to ameliorate and prevent psychosis. Of all these, lithium is the most persuasively tied to the actual prevention of suicide. But not everyone will respond to lithium, and not everyone will take it. And other medications also have an effect on suicidal behaviour. Most medications are problematic, but the research literature is consistent in showing that patients at high risk for suicide remain dangerously under-diagnosed and under-treated.

We know many things about suicide, but not enough. We need to have far more public awareness of how prevalent a killer suicide is, and we need to have far more public awareness of the symptoms and treatments for depression and other psychiatric disorders.

Families, schools, churches and synagogues, and university administrators need to learn more and they need to do more. They need to do far more. We require a society that is aware of this danger in its midst. We need a society that does not tolerate the intolerable. We need to do everything possible to prevent the kind of pain that went into the following poem, written by a 15-year-old boy two years before he killed himself:

> *Once ... he wrote a poem.*
> *And he called it 'Chops',*
> *Because that was the name of his dog, and*
> *that's what it was all about.*
> *And the teacher gave him an 'A'*
> *And a gold star.*
> *And his mother hung it on the kitchen door,*
> *and read it to all his aunts ...*

Once … he wrote another poem.
And he called it 'Question Marked Innocence',
Because that was the name of his grief, and
that's what it was all about.
And the professor gave him an 'A'
And a strange and steady look.
And his mother never hung it on the kitchen door
because he never let her see it …

Once, at 3 am … he tried another poem …
And he called it absolutely nothing, because
that's what it was all about.
And he gave himself an 'A'
And a slash on each damp wrist,
And hung it on the bathroom door because he
couldn't reach the kitchen.

Suicide is the worst, the most devastating outcome of mental illness. We can prevent more suicides than we do but we have social policies that do not take psychiatric mortalities as seriously as they take deaths from cancer, AIDS or heart disease. Social attitudes, and the stigma they reflect, not only hurt those with mental illness, they kill.

On the other hand, the tendency for society to romanticise mental illness and psychological suffering, by linking them to genius or artistic creativity, raises problems of another kind. This is particularly so because there is, in fact, some truth to the ancient belief voiced by Socrates. 'Madness', he said, 'comes from God, whereas sober sense is merely human.' And later, Aristotle asked: 'Why is it that all men who are outstanding in philosophy, poetry or the arts are melancholic?' It is an important question.

There is within most species, including man, a range in the ability and willingness to take risks. Temperaments and capacities vary. Some animals move faster and are more curious, more impulsive, more restless. Highly energetic, grasping and aggressive, they are drawn to new regions, different foods and disparate mates. Others wait, stand back, move collectively, and act less impetuously. The diversity of styles and temperaments serves the needs of the group, allowing it, as necessary, to push forward, or pull back, or to expand or conserve its collective energies.

Like other animals, human beings are diverse in their capacities and temperaments. Adaptive behaviours lurch with dispatch into maladaptive ones, a perhaps inevitable price that must be paid for a biological system that maintains the capacity to ratchet its responses in order to survive in a changing or dangerous environment. The balance between adaptive and pathological is often a tottery one, and it makes evolutionary sense that it should be so. George Schaller observed in his studies of the Seregenti lion and its prey that 'a galloping animal is precariously balanced'. Speed is necessary to save life but carries with it the risk of losing it.

We have, then, within ourselves, the capacity for extremes that will serve us well on occasion and badly on others. These extremes encompass not only rage and aggression but sadness and ecstasy, inertia and frenzied energy states, dullness and exploration.

Why do the genes and the volatile brain chemistry that underlie mental illness and suicide remain in our genetic make-up? Are they a part of the price we pay for diversity? Are the reckless and impulsive behaviours associated with many acts of suicide also associated with capacities integral to the survival of the species? Or do these pathologies exist independent of any adaptive value? The fact that a condition is widespread does not necessarily mean that it is adaptive.

Mood disorders, many believe, may give an advantage to individuals and their societies. Depression, characterised as it is by a conservation of energy during times of scant resources, a reduction of activity at times of non-negotiable threat, or a slowing or cessation of sexual behaviour when environmental conditions are poor, is a not-surprising biological reaction during times of change or stress. Depression in its mild forms may act as an alerting mechanism to other animals to act similarly and may, as some have argued, help to maintain a stable social hierarchy as well. The discontents and darkness of the depressive mind may also create – through the arts and philosophy – a useful perspective in the collective social awareness.

It is the temperamental, cognitive and behavioural elements of manic-depressive illness that provide the strongest evidence for a possible link between the occasional adaptive advantages of a severe illness, on the one hand, and suicide, on the other. Anne Sexton, who committed suicide after a long struggle with manic depression and alcoholism, wrote in one of her poems that the high-flying Icarus:

> … *glances up and is caught, wondrously tunneling*
> *into that hot eye. Who cares that he fell back to the sea?*

The 'wondrous tunneling' into the sun and subsequent falling back into the sea conjure an image of the dangerous relationship between exploration and recklessness. Mania, we know, is an aggressive and volatile state, but it is generative as well, an influential condition of contagious enthusiasms and energies. The elements that in part define mania – fearlessness, a fast and broad scattering of thoughts, an expansiveness of moods and ideas, utter certainty, the taking of inadvisable risks – often carry with them the power both to destroy and to create.

When the high-voltage manic brain slows, as it must, and its mood seeps down into depression, the crackling together of manic impetuousness with a black mood can be lethal. Suicide is the not-uncommon end point of a short-lived, violent, and yet, on occasion, fertile time.

The boldness and violence of the manic temperament may come at a cost, but there is strong evidence that manic depression and its milder forms can provide advantages to the individual, his or her kin, and society at large. Several studies have shown that many manic depressive patients and their relatives are uncommonly creative and academically successful. At least 20 investigations have found that highly creative individuals are much more likely than the general population to suffer from depression or manic-depressive illness. Clearly, mood disorders are not required for great accomplishment, and most people who suffer from mood disorders are not particularly accomplished. But the evidence is compelling that the creative are *disproportionately* affected by these conditions.

Suicide is also more common in highly creative or successful writers, artists, scientists and businessmen than it is in the general population. Most of these suicides are related to underlying depression, manic depression or alcoholism in combination with these mood disorders.

Percy Bysshe Shelley, who attempted suicide when young, said: 'But mark how beautiful an order has sprung from the dust and blood of this fierce chaos', and perhaps this is true. Extremes in emotions and thinking, when tightly yoked with a disciplined mind and high imagination, certainly can advance the arts, sciences and commerce. Suffering that may benefit a work of art or move the direction of a spiritual life may not be of such benefit to the life of the artist, however. Immoderate thought, and behaviour on the remotest ridges of experience, may end in death; yet some artists and explorers feel no choice but to go there. The pull between a life at the extremes and one in more moderate zones is fierce for many. 'It isn't possible to get values and colour', wrote Vincent van Gogh. 'You can't be at the pole and the equator at the same time. You must choose your own line, as I hope to do, and it will probably be colour.'

The ethical and societal implications of the association between mood disorders and creativity are staggeringly important but poorly understood. Many treatment strategies, for example, pay insufficient heed to the occasional, fleeting benefits manic-depressive illness can bestow on some individuals. Lithium and the anticonvulsant drugs are very effective therapies for mania and depression. Nevertheless, these drugs in high dosages can, in some individuals taking them, dampen general intellect, and limit emotional and perceptual range. For this reason, many patients stop taking their medications.

Left untreated, however, manic depressive illness tends to worsen over time – and, obviously, no one is creative when severely depressed, psychotic, in four-point restraints, or dead. The attacks of mania and depression tend to grow more frequent and more severe; without regular treatment, the disease can become less responsive to medication as well. In addition, patients with mood disorders frequently use other mood-altering substances such as alcohol, marijuana or cocaine, all of which can cause additional medical and psychiatric problems.

Most people who suffer from depression or manic depression are not unusually creative, and they reap few benefits from their illnesses; even those who are highly creative usually seek relief from their suffering. It would be irresponsible to romanticise extremely painful, destructive and potentially deadly diseases.

The real task of imaginative, compassionate and effective treatment is to give all patients more meaningful choices than they are now afforded. The extremes of depression and mania need to be controlled, of course, but without sacrificing crucial human emotions and experiences. Given time, and increasingly sophisticated research, psychiatrists will gain a better understanding of the complex biological basis for mood disorders. Eventually, the development of new drugs should make it possible to treat depression and manic-depressive illness in such a way that those aspects of temperament and cognition essential to the creative process remain intact.

The development of these more specific and less problematic therapies should be reasonably swift once scientists find the genes responsible for the disease. And, ultimately, however complicated the search, the genes for manic-depressive illness *will* be found: if not in the pedigrees of the studies reported so far, then in others yet to be published.

Major clinical and ethical issues will accompany the discovery of the genes responsible. Without question, individuals who have genetic diseases – including manic-depressive illness – will gain immeasurably from the knowledge obtained about early identification of children at high risk, from improved diagnostic systems, and from vastly improved and new treatments based upon an understanding of the illness at its molecular level.

Some of the ethical issues – for example, the accuracy and interpretation of diagnostic tests, the uses and abuses of selective abortion, the privacy of genetic information, insurance and employment discrimination – will be common to other genetic illnesses. Others will be unique to an illness that may confer advantage to society in the form of increased drive, restlessness, creativity, boldness, disinhibition, grandiosity and diversity of cognitive and temperamental styles.

The choices that an individual would make for himself or his children, may turn out to be quite different from those he would make as a member of society. It is a disconcerting thought.

Note: This lecture is based upon material written by the author in *Night falls fast: understanding suicide* (New York: Alfred A Knopf, Inc., 1999) and *Touched with fire: manic-depressive illness and the artistic temperament* (New York: Free Press, 1993).

Chapter 10

Living well, dying well (1)

Bert Keizer

I wish to consider the subject of living well and dying well, with particular reference to the role of medicine in or around these activities. It is my uncomfortable belief that medicine, as it is practised today in western Europe, hardly contributes to dying well. And the contribution of medicine to living well is on the whole grossly overrated, by doctors and patients alike.

Let us first try to say something about medicine's contribution to living well. Looking back into history, it would appear that people have always been pretty good at the simpler tasks of medicine. I'm not so sure about obstetrics – I've read some horrendous accounts there – but I'm thinking of how to deal with fractures and wounds. As to the many other ailments, please don't press me for a definition. There was an extensive use of herbs and less pleasant concoctions, which occasionally hit a target people didn't even know existed, and apart from that there was a lot of vomiting, purging, cupping, praying, blessing, sacrificing, laying on of hands, going on a pilgrimage, smoking it out, burning it away, giving it to the neighbours, passing it to an animal, scaring it away, showing it to the moon, magnetising, electrifying, mesmerising or hypnotising – and then all of a sudden we've arrived in the nineteenth century.

Every reasonably educated doctor would like to say that it wasn't until the nineteenth century that our profession gained a solid footing. What we describe as scientific medicine, rational medicine, is a view of the body and its functioning and malfunctioning that developed in the first half of the nineteenth century, a development which quickly gathered momentum and turned into one of the most remarkable upheavals of our social and physical lives.

One could speak after 1850 of the rise and rise and rise of modern medicine. Three discoveries were the most important initial steps:

- firstly, the advances in the study of the anatomical basis of the symptoms of disease
- secondly, the discovery of the bacterial causes of diseases, and the methods developed to avoid bacterial contamination

- thirdly, the discovery of anaesthesia, giving the surgeon time to perform an operation instead of having to hack his way through the panic of a struggling patient.

Many steps were to follow: antibiotics, insulin, increasing surgical sophistication, psychotropic medication, vaccination programmes against childhood diseases, open-heart surgery, kidney transplants, hip replacement, oral contraception, traumatology, intensive care techniques, and so on, but not *ad infinitum*. I cannot enumerate all that has come our way, but I would like to point out to you one or two consequences.

Because medicine has become so clever, as it might seem, at removing so much suffering, the many kinds of suffering against which it is powerless have fallen into disregard.

We are so intoxicated by the marvellous successes of medicine in certain situations that we believe this to be applicable to all the other situations as well. And if not now, then certainly in the future. So we think that a patient's complaint will, after diagnostic procedures, always be traced to a diagnosis and thus a treatment will ensue – the cough, the chest X-ray, the pneumonia and then the penicillin. What we don't want to know is that in many situations, far more than we usually guess, this sequence doesn't occur at all. In fact in many cases we get stuck after diagnosis, for there is no treatment. We cannot cure a stroke, or Alzheimer's disease, or Parkinson's disease, or multiple sclerosis, or motor neurone disease, or schizophrenia, or nicotine addiction, or osteoporosis, or, most famously, and least believed of all, we cannot cure cancer.

The war on cancer, as it is fondly called, is one of the most fascinating aspects of medicine in the second half of the twentieth century. The best brains in the best laboratories all over the western world have spent five decades now at the cost of billions and billions on research into the cure for cancer. The great breakthrough has for 50 years been 'just around the corner'.

The cure for cancer resembles the coming of 'true socialism', which had been about to occur in the late Soviet Union for more than seven decades, but never made its actual appearance. Oncology seems to be in much the same position.

This is so fascinating, because it offers an insight into the nature of medicine: medicine doesn't always have to deliver the goods, but can still send the bill. In that respect it resembles prayer: you ask for something but you don't blame your method if you don't obtain a result.

When we consider the whole area of medical practice we will discern a small bright circle at the centre where a number of treatments are gathered that have been proved to be efficacious. Beyond this centre we stumble into a twilight zone, where we find a number of treatments that might some day justifiably be placed in the bright centre but have as yet not *earned that place*. Beyond this zone again, darkness reigns. Here we find a vast array of doing things with people who are ill. These approaches are silly, cruel, dishonest, innocent, cynical, harmless or unhealthy, both in intent and in their effects. Doctors place many more of their doings in the hallowed centre than is scientifically justifiable. Patients are hardly aware of the murkier zones at all. They reckon all is in the centre, or almost there anyway.

Why this overestimation? The clear and simple answer is that we don't want to die. Because of this mythical demand for eternal life that medicine is to satisfy, I believe it is impossible to take the myth out of medicine, just as impossible as taking the glamour out of war. And while war shouldn't be glamorous, nor medicine mythical, it cannot be helped as we are so helpless in the face of disease, incapacity, decay, old age, death. When threatened by adversity on a sufficiently crushing scale, it is impossible to keep your wits about you, whatever philosophers tell you.

The actual contribution of medicine to living well is of course impossible to assess. But what doctors and patients *think* about this contribution is beyond reason and unfounded.

A second cause of the overestimation of medicine and what it can achieve lies in a misconception of science. Ludwig Wittgenstein said in the *Tractatus*: 'We feel that even when *all possible* scientific questions have been answered, the problems of life remain completely untouched.' I think what Wittgenstein means is this: around suffering there's always the question *why*. So when a patient asks 'Why am I to die?', and the doctor responds with a lengthy disquisition on the insufficiency of her coronaries, the leak in her mitral valve, the accumulation of fluids in the lungs, the faltering oxygenation of her blood and so on, going into the resulting mitochondrial changes in her cortical tissue if you like, the patient will interrupt all this physiology and will ask: 'Never mind all that, I meant why *me*?'

This is the point where the doctor breaks off and holds his tongue, ideally, because he realises the difference between a physiological and an existential question. Usually nothing of all this happens of course: the patient is dismissed, the why-me question is buried under a deluge of diagnostic moves. The sad misunderstanding being that a blood test, an X-ray, a scan, can ever tell us anything about why we are here. Since God left the premises, also somewhere in the nineteenth century, we have been lumbered with a certain ignorance about the purpose of life. It seems to me that this ignorance is eagerly buried underneath a pile of tests, none of which can show us why we suffer.

Why does this matter? First of all: it hurts. It hurts when you get faceless biochemistry offered while you are trying to digest your suffering religiously, metaphysically or psychologically. The doctor as priest is the man or woman who succeeds not so much in curing a disease as in explaining the disease in such terms as to make it credible and palatable – metaphysically digestible one could say.

Secondly, this matters because this misguided chase after scientific answers ('Can't you see I'm busy?') seems to absolve the doctor from what I take to be precisely one-half of our duty: to stand by your patient in his suffering. Doctors are very keen on taking away misery, well who isn't, and it is in this role that they like to shine. The silly reverence for scientific questions and their answers ignores the suffering that cannot be taken away.

Thirdly, the overestimation of the importance of scientific responses adds insult to injury: offering chemotherapy in certain stages of cancer, where its application is plainly cruel; admitting demented elderly patients to intensive care units, where they die unnecessarily painful deaths. There's a whole host of procedures that flaunt the Hippocratic dictum: don't make it worse. Ignoring a person's suffering because all the attention is focused on biochemical parameters is a daily sin in medical practice.

To some of you all this may sound unlikely, irresponsible, exaggerated, unfounded, hysterical even, but I assure you a certain shrillness in statement is necessary in order to rise above the horrendous din that the opposite view is usually making, and has been making for some 150 years now. I am not scoffing at medicine; I am merely trying to state what it can and cannot do.

So much for medicine's contribution to living well. Next we move on to the subject of dying well.

All patients must die. Doctors are so keen on statistics these days that I will gladly serve their interest: the percentage here is 100!

I would like to compare two deaths, that of Byron and of my own father, to show that ignorance can be just as awful as knowledge in its effect on a patient's suffering.

In 1824, Byron was 36 and found himself in Greece fighting for their independence against the Turks. The military scene was outrageously corrupt and he fell dangerously ill in the swamps of Missolonghi. He told his doctor, Julius Millingen, that he was heartily sick of life, 'but the apprehension of two things now haunt my mind'. He added: 'I picture myself slowly expiring on a bed of torture, or terminating my days like Swift – a grinning idiot.' Bed of torture it was to be. In the words of his biographer, Leslie Marchand, Byron had a healthy dread of the remedies of his medical men, the doctors Bruno and Millingen, who knew of only one way out of medical trouble: bleeding. On the morning of the 10th of April Bruno recommended this procedure, but Byron refused. The doctor gave him castor oil instead and put him in a hot bath. Three days later Bruno prescribed antimony powder against the fever, as Byron absolutely refused bleeding and the application of leeches. On the fifth day Dr Millingen was called in and together they tried to convince him to submit to bleeding. Byron became irritated, saying that 'he knew well that the lancet had killed more people than the lance'. They kept on administering pills and cathartics, and at noon the next day they returned again to demand his blood, but Byron refused, as annoyed as before. He told them that: 'Drawing blood from a nervous patient is like loosening the cords of a musical instrument, the tones of which are already defective for want of sufficient tension.'

In spite of this beautiful phrasing, Dr Bruno continued to plead for permission to bleed him, but Byron steadfastly refused and asked for the company of Parry, a rough old soldier with whom he felt more at ease than with the menacing doctors. When Parry left late in the evening, Byron was seized by a violent spasmodic coughing that caused him to vomit. Dr Bruno threatened him with inflammation of the lungs if he did not allow himself to be bled, and Byron at last gave in and promised his veins to Bruno the following day. But in the morning Byron felt better and retracted his promise, which set off a violent altercation between him and his doctors that ended in his throwing out his arm to them and exclaiming: 'Come; you are, I see, a damned set of butchers. Take away as much blood as you will, but have done with it.' They removed a pound, but the relief obtained did not correspond, noted Dr Millingen, 'to the hopes we had anticipated'. Two hours later they took another pound, after which he felt alleviated or exhausted. Anyway, he fell asleep. The quality of his pulse remaining the same, they proposed a third bleeding on the basis of Byron's complaint of a numbness in the fingers. In his lucid moments Byron resisted their further efforts. This did not mean that he was rid of his tormentors for now they gave him purgatives instead.

On the seventh day of his troubles he was continuously delirious and two more physicians were called in. They, for once, did not bleed him but gave him some China bark, water and wine, and applied two blisters on the inside of his thighs. On the eighth day it was clear to all that Byron was going down rapidly and Dr Bruno again came up with his favourite remedy: he applied 12 leeches to the temples of his dying patient and extricated two pounds of blood. From now on Byron was intermittently delirious. The doctors had decided on another purgation: 'a clyster of senna, castor oil and three ounces of Epsom salts.' Incredibly Byron got out of bed at six in the evening to relieve himself. 'Damned doctors,' he muttered, 'I can scarcely stand.' Back in bed he lost consciousness and the doctors again applied leeches to his temples. The blood flowed freely all night and he died at six in the evening of the following day.

This harrowing account of adding medical insult to physical injury seems so absurd that one might wonder what on earth these people thought they were doing. I think the doctors Bruno and Millingen meant no harm. And yet they did cause harm, by ignoring their patient and sticking to their textbooks.

This same thing still occurs, and not rarely. One hundred-and-seventy years later, in May 1994, my father was 87 years old, a dedicated smoker of roll-ups all his life and in recent years increasingly short of breath on account of emphysema. One of the most ill-starred meetings in modern medicine is that between a frail, defenceless old man nearing the end of his life, and an agile young intern at the beginning of his career.

Soon after my father's admission into hospital, chest X-rays were taken and he was seen by a chest physician. He prescribed oxygen, mucolytics, antibiotics and physiotherapy. My father did not improve. A pulmonary embolism could not with all certainty be excluded and so he was put on anticoagulants. He was very feverish and anxious, and at night he was delirious.

The doctor suspected an element of cardiac failure so he called in the cardiologist. After another set of X-rays and an ECG had duly been performed, this colleague added diuretics to the medication, and went his way. The patient however did not improve at all; on the contrary, he seemed to be slipping away from us.

On his sixth day in hospital he passed a bloody stool, probably caused by impacted faecal matter damaging the intestinal mucosa on its way out. Now the gastroenterologist was called in. Of course he advised a colonoscopy, to exclude the possibility of cancer. In order for a colonoscopy to be possible my father was given about the same amount of purgatives as Lord Byron had had to sustain, and on the evening before the procedure my mother found him drenched in his own mess. He had totally lost his bearings at this stage and was restless at nights, trying to climb out of bed, forgetting he had a catheter. In order to prevent these hazardous nocturnal excursions he was given a tranquilliser, haloperidol.

On the seventh day he could hardly speak because of the tremor induced by the haloperidol, which made him all shaky and tremulous. He was taken for the colonoscopy, nevertheless, and the doctor found a polyp in his colon, which he proceeded to remove with a cauteriser, almost burning a hole in the intestinal wall, as he told me excitedly later, and certainly causing considerable blood loss.

On the ninth day one of the nurses came with the suggestion that my father was probably an Alzheimer patient. The thought being, if there was a thought behind this suggestion, that if they mutter incomprehensibly, they're probably demented. A psychiatrist and a neurologist were called in to evaluate this possibility, a brain scan was arranged, and admission to a nursing home was put on the agenda.

He had hardly been eating and was lying passively in bed, and now severe bedsores were threatening. In order to do something about this the dermatologist was called in. During these ten days my father had been seen by an internist consultant, a pulmonary physician, a cardiologist, a gastroenterologist, a psychiatrist, a neurologist and a dermatologist. He had been subjected to four X-rays, uncomfortable but not unsettling, many blood tests, and the gruesome procedure of bowel cleaning prior to the colonoscopy. Even if he had not been feverish and sedated he would have been completely baffled after so many encounters.

The net outcome of all this high-flown medical expertise was that he had turned from a very ill old man into a physical and mental wreck with whom it was almost impossible to communicate. When, to top it all, the consultant wanted to call in a nephrologist because of a touch of renal failure that was now showing up in his blood tests, we finally called a halt to all this and asked his GP to intervene.

The family doctor put in his dentures, then looked for and thoroughly cleaned his glasses, and after a lot of fumbling managed to get his hearing-aid properly positioned. He then sat down with him and they spoke for about half an hour. When asked what he really wanted, my father said he wanted to be left alone in order to die in peace. He was moved to a geriatric ward in a neighbouring hospital, was given some morphine, and died peacefully three days later. A week after his death, the pathologist called me to report on the benignant aspect of the polyp removed.

I believe that a death-bed like my father's is so annoying to the internal medicine consultant, because all his knowledge, *all* his knowledge, doesn't show the way to a cure here. There is no blood test that tells you when to stop calling in other doctors, hoping they have a cure. The point is, as Beckett would say: 'You're human, and there's no cure for that.'

You might say that Byron was as pestered with what we now call ignorance, as many a present-day patient with what we now regard as knowledge, and the contribution of modern medicine to dying well is, I would say, disastrous. We should be ashamed of the way we seize on the dying in their frailty, blinded as we are by the fatal notion that a man's potassium level is more telling than his innermost thoughts about life and death.

To sum up, then, in the nineteenth century scientific medicine was born. Its success in alleviating suffering was so immense as to leave us all over-impressed. However, not *all* physical suffering can or ever will be taken away by medicine, and yet we act as if medicine can do this, or will soon be capable of doing this. Paradoxically, this leads to increased suffering, especially in the hour of death, when the scientific analysis of bodily events ignores the sadness of parting from life. Our real questions, in Wittgenstein's sense, are not scientific. And we would do well, when talking about choices around death, to be aware of the understandable but therefore no less harmful blindness of one of the principal actors in the last act of life – the doctor with his scientific obsession.

References

1. Wittgenstein L. *Tractatus logico-philosophicus*. London: Routledge, 1999.
2. Nicolson H. *Byron: the last journey*. London: Prion Books, 1999 (first published 1924).
3. Beckett S. *Molloy*. London: Calder and Boyars, 1966.

Chapter 11

Living well, dying well (2)

Rowan Williams

'Only humans know death because the ego fixes time.'[1] A very brief formulation, but a pregnant one: if we are more than bundles of sensation – as we are, since we can order and narrate our sensations – there is no escape from the knowledge of limit. We remember that the stories of others have an end, and while we may, particularly when we're young, experience this knowledge as rather abstract, we are bound to become more directly aware as time passes that any and every project of ours has a terminus. Knowing about death is, it's been said, the price we pay for self-awareness, for that dimension of our existence that is over and above the purely reactive. And that of course is why it is a paradoxical and difficult knowledge. Our self-awareness secures this territory in which our life is seen as 'more than reactive'; we see our activity in a more intense way; and then, with this comes the awareness that we are ultimately wholly passive, in the sense that something will finally be done to us over which we have no control whatsoever.

The writer I quoted at the beginning of this talk, Ernest Becker, is probably best remembered for his extraordinary book *The denial of death*, in which he traced some of the characteristic pathologies of human society in general and modern society in particular to the refusal to accept this ultimate passivity. We are involved, he argued, in a struggle to define ourselves as self-created or self-caused, and we work intensively at denying not only death but dependence, with the result that we look for solutions through what we can grasp as 'heroic' behaviour, the shoring up of childish omnipotence. In societies with powerful authority patterns (religious or secular) there is usually some kind of accepted style of heroism on offer – military achievement, ascetic self-denial, superhuman productivity. When authority decays, so does heroism; which leaves us with just the same underlying panic about death and dependence, but no readily available social carriers for their denial. No one is providing us with models for the transcendence or avoidance of mortality; so either we face the truth about death (which might mean a number of things, and I'll return to this) or we mess around with consciousness to scale down the pain of awareness. Addictive behaviour takes over; and Becker identifies this not only with the obvious patterns we see in late modernity (drugs, obsessional consumption, and so on), but also with our absorption in the search for the 'true self'. The irony is, he suggests, that psychiatry, which gives us so many of the tools we need to understand our terror of death and the mechanisms of avoidance, has itself become a mechanism of avoidance, holding out to us the promise that there is, somewhere, a state of mind whose equilibrium will miraculously remove our fear. He is scathing about the pseudo-spirituality of ecstasy, the oceanic state, the recovery of childlike spontaneity. How, he wants to know, can I be an adult who knows that I am going to die: a person free from the falsity of heroics, classical or modern, and the illusions of infantile spirituality?

How he answers this, and what we might make of his answers, I leave aside for now because what needs emphasising at this point, I think, is the clear connection that is being made between living well and – if not exactly dying well – living in expectation of death. Death is not first and foremost a threat to be overcome, but a fact: we shall not be able to avoid this ultimate passivity – our action meets a brick wall. If we begin to grasp this, without resentment or illusion, it alters what we are able to think about our actions themselves. They are in some sense relativised; they can't be guaranteed success or immortality in their effects because the point arrives where one must relinquish control over what one does and its results. In other words, what I think of as living well will be shaped by what sense I make of death; and what I make of death will be shaped by how I have understood what it is for me to live well. A circle of interpretation, but not a vicious one: as I discover that I shall die, I return to question what I hope for my life, and as that takes shape I clarify my attitude towards death.

A word of clarification before going on. It may seem that religious beliefs of certain kinds offer a short cut: there is life after death, so death is only an episode in a continuing story. Well, popular religiosity has signs of such a view ('slipping into the next room' and so on), but there are more complex elements in the tradition as a whole. Death is an absolute reality, which is quite properly seen as dreadful at first sight; it marks the limit of those actions that will decide what happens afterwards (which is certainly not just continuance in a vaguely similar environment). Only when death is separated from judgement in religious talk can there be anything like the consoling myth that death is an interruption in a single story. But, of course, that is the separation that religiosity has encouraged in much of the modern period.

This is why Becker has no qualms in identifying religious belief not as a form of denying death but as a desirable, if not necessary, element in confronting it without illusion. Very suggestively, he proposes that religious faith is the intrinsic enemy of heroism in the usual sense; it puts our actions under a transcendent scrutiny that we simply cannot get at or reproduce, and so it should foster reticence, irony, the awareness of fallibility. The traditional psychoanalytic suspicion of religion, he claims, has damaged the analytic project and helped breed the utopian narcissism that passes for psychiatry in much of our culture (hard words here for Brown and Maslow, and even Jung); the truth is that the heart of the language of faith is about not projecting either our terror or our hope onto each other. No human other is our saviour; no human other is our absolute destroyer. Belief in God 'projects' right outside the system of human interrelation, setting us all before a reality to which we are all equally kin and equally strange.

But how does this impact specifically on the relation between living well and being aware of death? Negatively, it blocks off the more obvious and destructive forms of transference, looking for heroic possibilities in the will of the group or the leader; though a Christian might be allowed to say that Becker is perhaps a bit generous in not pointing out how religious behaviour patterns can in historical fact themselves produce their own murderous heroisms. Positively though, I suspect that we'd need to say something like this. The goodness of what I do is, in a religious context, understood as and only as an alignment to some fundamental pattern of agency or purpose; I don't define what's good – goodness is not to be seen in terms of what serves or expresses my inner truth or whatever (think about this; it is still a fairly strongly counter-cultural notion). What's more, for all the major religious traditions, the good is achieved only by corporate action. The substantial goods of the moral world cannot be attained by summing up or adding together sets of individual achievements, because these goods are seen as inseparable from the openness of mutuality – not in the sense of polite tolerance but in the more robust sense of knowing where my own resources fall short and not being afraid to call on the strengths of another. The good is essentially co-operative. So if my action has limits, if it runs against the brick wall of death, that is not, for the believer, the end of the story. What I have done will feed into continuing action; and this is seen not just as more human action but finally as a making space for the action of the creator. When I am forced to resign control and effectiveness, I have to believe that certain things continue to be done, and that my part in their doing has been neither all-important nor insignificant. If I can see what I do as part of this wider 'being done', I may learn to face the ultimate frustration of death with less lying and panic, even though I may still fear (because I go also to be judged, to be told a fuller truth about myself than I could have discovered).

This is given a strong practical turn in a discussion by the American ethicist Stanley Hauerwas on 'Suffering, death and medicine'. Two points in particular are salient here. First, he observes that suffering is not a word with a simple definition – we all suffer, to the extent that we are all having done to us things we did not choose. How such suffering is to be calibrated, whether it is ever possible for an observer to assess what constitutes intolerable suffering, is an immensely complicated question, because of the varied ways in which individuals 'absorb' suffering into what they believe about their lives as a whole. If you think that suffering is one and only one sort of thing that simply needs to be removed by professional care (medical or psychological), you deny implicitly the importance of what Hauerwas calls 'incorporating suffering into our moral projects'.[2] This is not at all to say, he insists, that suffering is to be accepted passively and uncomplainingly; where suffering cannot be connected with our 'moral project', where it can only be seen as contingent, every effort should be made to alleviate it. But even where it can be 'humanised' and moralised, it may still be right to work against it. Hauerwas is simply challenging the assumption that suffering can be seen on a mechanical model, as always an identifiable target that can be acted on and taken away. His counter-proposal is that, whether or not intervention is possible or judged desirable, the bare fact of suffering is first and foremost a moral challenge: can this be taken into the picture I have of myself, can I make my story out of this? If, as he claims, medicine has to be an art as well as a science, it must beware of disregarding the moral issue even when it is working for alleviation. This is perhaps the model that lies behind much of the philosophy of the hospice movement, but it should not be alien to the whole understanding of medical practice in any context.

And this leads on to Hauerwas's second main point. What happens when we appear to be faced with a choice between suffering and death? When there is an issue about relieving suffering at the cost of hastening death (let alone directly procuring death)? His response is to imagine himself faced with some such decision; and his conclusion is that to phrase the choice in such a way actually begs the question. We do not by any means necessarily try to 'balance' suffering and death in such circumstances, he argues. A decision for accelerating death might be taken because a debilitating long-term course of treatment might imperil my doing 'the kinds of things I would like to do'.[2] Conversely, though Hauerwas doesn't spell it out, deciding that treatment should continue might rest on a decision to experiment with new challenges, or to spare someone close to you what they might see as a premature bereavement, or an awareness that your endurance might be significant to someone else. What these decisions emphatically are not is 'purely medical'. In Hauerwas's terms, the issue is about how what happens 'fits into the narrative of one's life'.[2]

This might be taken as grounds for softening the conventional Christian view of euthanasia; but I don't think this is Hauerwas's intention at all. To forestall these issues by deciding to intervene oneself or request direct medical intervention whose prime purpose is to cause death would be, in Hauerwas's scheme, as in traditional Christian ethics, an act of violence, an attempt to take possession of the future and to deny passivity of any kind in the face of death. This remains true in the Christian framework even when such a decision is taken with a subjective sense of helplessness, or in deep spiritual anguish. And in terms of the perspective outlined earlier in this talk, it might also be a refusal to raise the question of what effects my action has in the whole process of actions towards the good, or actions making space for God. To the extent that a decision to bring about death might be saying that this condition or this situation can't be understood in the context of a life 'narrated' in relation to God and the body of believers, it becomes problematic: it cannot bear good news for others (assuming that the relief of the sheer discomfort and frustration of someone witnessing pain they cannot remove or alleviate is not itself good news in the Christian sense). For Christian moralists, bringing about one's death must always be a kind of denial of death, an attempt to make one's own what is done to one. It remains importantly distinct from making sense of death as it approaches, living in the face of death. But I'd emphasise that this is a prohibition on euthanasia whose intelligibility rests essentially on a particular theological view of life – not a belief that preserving life at all costs is the basic religious value (it clearly isn't), not even the belief that life is 'sacred', but the belief that lives are deeply implicated with each other to the extent that violence against oneself (even in extreme circumstances) has to be violence against others as well. There are other arguments against euthanasia in the more pragmatic field, but it is helpful to recognise those that come specifically from a theological stance – if only to be clear that, even if euthanasia were legalised in some form and pragmatic anxieties overcome, it could not be a course of action endorsed by Christians.

Returning to the main theme, the central thesis I have been defending is that living well entails discovering how not to deny death, how to recognise and avoid the traps of 'heroism', how to be prepared to think through suffering (and death) in the light of what Hauerwas calls the 'moral project' – which, I should argue, means for the Christian believer an education in awareness of how there are no purely individual moral projects. This, I suggest, both helps to deal with the unavoidable frustration of all human projects and puts a question against the ultimate spiritual legitimacy of any decision deliberately to take command of one's dying by positive intervention. Margot Waddell, in a recent book on the growth of the personality, *Inside lives*, writes of how personalities 'capable of experience' are formed, and continue to be formed right up to the moment of death.[3] It is a suggestive formulation; the implication is that our various denials of death make us in the long term incapable of experience; that is, of that conscious receiving and reworking of what is done to us that enables narrative, the sense of a continuous self.

We began with Becker's assertion that humans alone are aware of death because of the necessary relation of the ego to time; the animal consciousness, as far as we know, exists in a sort of unbroken present, while we remember and anticipate and cannot imagine consciousness in any other mode. But there is a paradox emerging. Precisely as we learn what it is to act in awareness of our action's place in the lives and actions of others and in relation to God, we become detached in some degree from the short-term effect of action. We become, in other words, more attuned to the present moment, not by a reversion to pre-human consciousness, but in an intensifying of the sense of being part of a wider reality and not being 'responsible' for the whole. We become more capable of contemplation, in the broadest sense. And it may be that the effect of living in the presence of death is to be free for contemplation (and that the absence of the contemplative dimension is a sure sign of the denial of death). Medical struggles with issues of life and death are not, in the nature of the case, oriented to teaching contemplation. But, reverting to the importance of medicine as art as well as science, we do well to suspect too facile appeals to the purely medical, if that means the mechanistic. Much of what I have said is summed up with some poignancy by Gillian Rose, in words she wrote during her own terminal illness about the peculiar variety of 'heroism' espoused by a particular kind of mechanistic surgeon: 'They do not understand, as part of their profession, "death" in the non-medical sense, nor therefore "life" in the meaningful sense, inclusive of death. When they fail to "cure", according to their own lights, they deal out death.'[4] But perhaps it is no more difficult for physicians and surgeons to include death in life than it is for the rest of us, restlessly looking for ways of avoidance and assurances of control.

References

1. Becker E. *The denial of death*. New York: Macmillan, 1973.
2. Hauerwas, S. *Suffering presence: theological reflections on medicine, the mentally handicapped, and the church*. Indiana, USA: University of Notre Dame Press, 1986/Edinburgh: T&T Clark, 1988.
3. Waddell M. *Inside lives: psychoanalysis and the growth of the personality*. London: Duckworth, 1998.
4. Rose G. *Love's work*. London: Chatto and Windus, 1995.

Chapter 12

Health in the city (1)

Julian Le Grand

It is, of course, a great honour to be asked to give this lecture as a Millennial Fellow. It is also something of an embarrassment. For, when I was approached about a year ago, I agreed to give this talk on a subject – health and the city – about which I knew relatively little, and in an area – which I suppose one might term health geography – about which I knew even less. As one does, especially when the event is a year away, I hoped that by the time the moment came I could be up to speed on the latest debates in the area and even perhaps be able to make a small contribution to those debates. As so often, this was a triumph of hope over experience and, in the event, all that I have been able to do is to unearth some puzzles. These I shall put before you tonight in the hope that people in the audience with a much greater degree of knowledge and experience in the area may be able to resolve them.

The first puzzle arises from the 1998 *Health survey for England*.[1] This is part of a survey carried out every year for the Department of Health by the National Centre for Social Research and the Department of Epidemiology and Public Health at the Royal Free and University College Medical School. Taking a representative sample of around 20,000 people living in private households, it asks a variety of questions on a wide range of topics, including self-reported health, use of health services, health-related behaviour, such as smoking and diet, and standard demographic and socio-economic factors, such as income, occupation and family structure. Also, each year it addresses a specific topic, such as the prevalence of a particular disease.

In 1998, the year on which I am focusing, it concentrated on cardiovascular disease. As well as the normal range of questions, respondents were asked whether they suffered from any of the following conditions: angina, heart attack, stroke, heart murmur, abnormal heart rhythm, 'other heart trouble', diabetes and high blood pressure, and (if they responded affirmatively) if they had ever had the condition diagnosed by a doctor. Informants were classified as having a particular condition only if they reported that the diagnosis was confirmed by a doctor (or a nurse in the case of blood pressure).[2]

Now, for each respondent in 1998, interviewers provided their own assessment of the area in which the respondent lived as to whether it was urban, suburban or rural. Although the results classified in this way were not published in the survey report,[3] the National Centre for Social Research has been good enough to provide me with some of the relevant data. That on self-reported health is summarised in Figure 12.1, based on Table A.1 in the Appendix. Each adult was asked to rate his or her health according to a five-point scale: very good, good, fair, poor, very poor. Figure 12.1 shows the proportion from each area type that reported good or very good.

Fig. 12.1 *Health survey for England:* percentage of adults reporting 'good' or 'very good' health

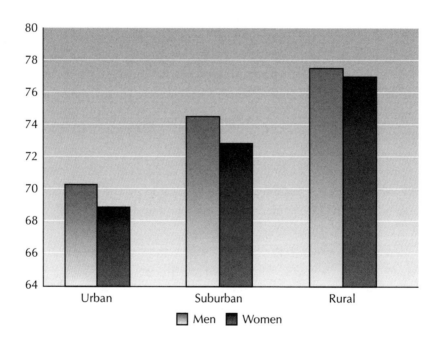

Source: Appendix Table A.1

It is apparent from Figure 12.1 that the proportion of adults who report their health as good or very good in rural areas is, at 78 per cent for men and 77 per cent for women, much higher than in urban areas (70 per cent men, 69 per cent women) and indeed higher than in suburban areas (75 per cent men, 73 per cent women). So far, not very surprising; most people, I suspect, would be happy to believe that cities – crowded, dirty and polluted – are on the whole unhealthier places to live than the countryside – empty, wholesome and clean.

This picture of rural superiority is supported by another result from the *Health survey for England*. Figure 12.2 shows a rather more specific kind of self-reported health: the proportion of adults reporting a long-standing illness that limits their activities in comparison with people of their own age. Here it is the suburban areas who have the highest reporting rates for both men and women, followed by urban. Again rural reporting rates are below them both, although it has to be said that the differences are not large.

Fig. 12.2 *Health survey for England:* percentage of adults reporting a limiting long-standing illness

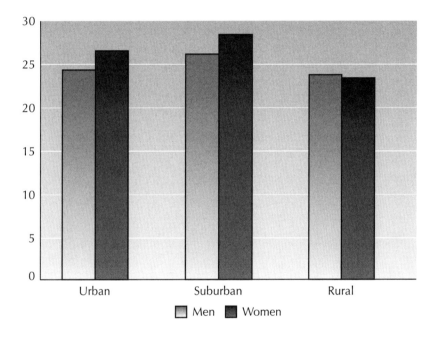

Source: Appendix Table A.1

However, the results for the prevalence of cardiovascular disease – perhaps a more objective measure of illness – give a rather different picture, illustrated in Figure 12.3. This shows the proportion of adults with a CVD condition, where a CVD condition is defined as any doctor-diagnosed heart murmur, diabetes, angina, heart attack, irregular heartbeat, stroke or other heart trouble. It is apparent that rural CVD is higher than urban. Indeed for women, rural CVD is higher than for suburban, although not for men. The same results hold if high blood pressure is included together with the others as an indicator of CVD.

Fig. 12.3 *Health survey for England:* percentage of adults diagnosed with CVD

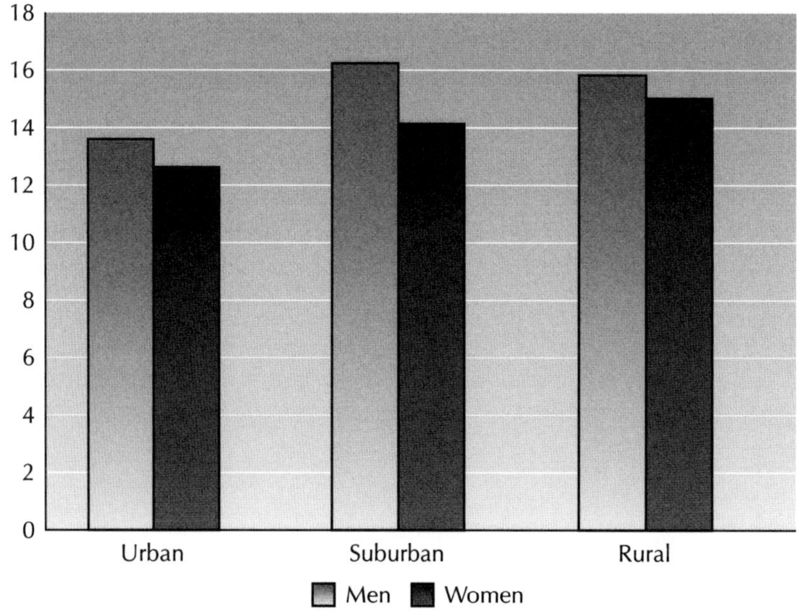

Source: Appendix Table A.1

Care should be taken in interpreting this data: some of the differences are quite small and may not always be significant. But, for what they are worth, they suggest that those in urban areas – that is, in cities – *feel* in worse health than those in rural and suburban areas, but *are* actually in better health. And that is the puzzle: if it is true, why are the inhabitants of cities getting better but feeling worse than their country brethren?

Now there are a number of possible resolutions of this puzzle. One is to say, simply, that it does not exist; or, more specifically, that the Survey data concerning self-reported illness or that concerning the prevalence of actual disease are misleading, and that in fact the two phenomena do actually go in the same direction. So far as self-reported illness is concerned, we can check the *Health survey for England* results against the results of the 1991 Census. It will be recalled that the latter asked a question concerning limiting long-standing illness, similar in form to that of the *Health survey for England*. Analysis of the responses to this question by urban and rural areas by Chris Denham and Ian White did in fact find the same phenomenon. Rural areas, not only in England but also, and indeed even more so, in Scotland and Wales, had a lower proportion of residents in households reporting a limiting long-standing illness than in urban areas.[4] The relevant figures are: England, 12.2 per cent urban and 10.1 per cent rural; Wales, 17.0 per cent urban and 13.7 per cent rural; Scotland, 12.9 per cent urban and 9.5 per cent rural.[5]

Unfortunately, I have been unable to find little information on more objective measures of illness to complement (or contradict) the *Health survey for England* results in that area. Mortality rates would be an obvious candidate, but although a great deal of mortality data by geographical area is published, it is not in a form that permits direct urban/rural comparisons of the kind undertaken here. There is a good deal of international evidence on urban/rural comparisons of various kinds, but that is conflicting.[6]

One study that I did find is most interesting, but not exactly contemporary: in fact, it refers to 1839. It comes from Edwin Chadwick's famous report on the sanitary conditions of the labouring classes in Great Britain, which I show you as a curiosity in Table 12.1.

Table 12.1 Average age at death (years) in three urban areas and one rural area for three groups in 1839

	Professional persons and gentry	*Tradesmen*	*Labourers*
Manchester	38	20	17
Liverpool	35	22	15
Bethnal Green	45	26	16
Rutland	52	41	38

Source: Flynn M W, editor. *Report on the sanitary conditions of the labouring population of Great Britain by Edwin Chadwick, 1842.* Edinburgh: Edinburgh University Press.

If we may digress for a moment and examine Table 12.1, it does have a number of striking aspects. One is the relative youth at which people died in that period, even if they were relatively well off and lived in rural areas. In Jane Austen's *Sense and sensibility*, published in 1811, the 17-year-old Marianne ('sensibility') dismisses a potential suitor, Colonel Brandon, as, at the wrong side of 35, an absolute old bachelor 'who must have long outlived every sensation'; however, she does acknowledge that he may live 'twenty years longer'. However, had Colonel Brandon been living in rural Rutland 30 years later, he might not have lived even that long, for the average age-at-death for professional persons and gentry there was 52. Another aspect of note is the large differences between the social classes in all four areas; the social class health inequalities that are so central to much of the present debate concerning public health are nothing new. Of more relevance for our immediate purposes is the difference between Rutland and the other areas for each class, with the average age-at-death in Rutland being around half as much again for professionals and gentry, and around twice that for tradesmen and labourers. Interestingly, it was this difference in health between town and country that sparked off a lot of the concerns of nineteenth-century social reformers in Britain, including Edwin Chadwick himself, and the Compiler of Abstracts to the Registrar General, William Farr.[7,8] Since then, of course, the focus has switched to differences in mortality between the social classes; and it is therefore perhaps not so surprising that it is difficult to find contemporary published data on mortality between rural and urban areas. But it does mean that it is difficult to check whether this health superiority of rural areas was still manifest at the turn of the twenty-first century – or whether, as the CVD data from the *Health survey for England* suggests, it has disappeared.[9]

To return to our puzzle. It might be possible to explain it in terms of health perceptions and knowledge. It could be that inhabitants of cities are more knowledgeable about health matters than those who live in the country; this would make them more anxious about their own levels of health and therefore less likely to report good health. The difficulty with this is that, if it were true, one might expect to find significant differences in health-damaging behaviour between town and country, with the former engaging in much less than the latter; but in fact, the *Health survey for England* suggests that only few such differences exist. There are no significant differences between urban and rural areas in alcohol consumption or in body weight. Rural men do have a much higher fat intake than urban men; but rural women do not. One area where there is a big difference is smoking (see Figure 12.4). Unfortunately, this is the wrong direction for this particular thesis, with urban men and women smoking considerably more than their rural counterparts.

Fig. 12.4 *Health survey for England:* percentage of adults reporting themselves as current smokers

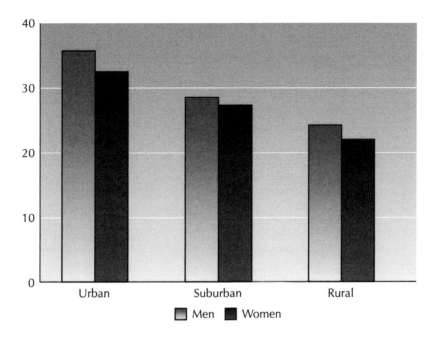

Source: National Centre for Social Research

Another reaction is to accept the phenomenon as correct, but to suggest that it has nothing to do with differences in the urban/rural context as such. Rather, it arises from differences in the demographic or socio-economic composition of the relevant populations. In other words, the data may be picking up the differences between poor and rich populations or between younger and older ones, rather than geographical ones: they show up as geographic differences purely because the relevant areas have different concentrations of these types of populations.

It is certainly true that there are differences in the demographic and socio-economic compositions of the areas. The survey found that rural populations are generally older, with a smaller proportion of under-16s and a larger proportion of over-65s than either urban or suburban populations. Rather more surprisingly, they are also richer, with a higher proportion of both men and women in the top income brackets and in the highest social classes (see Appendix Table A.2).

However, this does not really resolve the puzzle, but rather generates new ones. If the rural population is generally more elderly than the urban one, then why is it not reporting more ill health? And, while the differences in reported morbidity do seem consistent with what we know about the positive link between socio-economic status and health, with the richer rural areas reporting less illness than the poorer urban ones, they are not consistent with the data on CVD – which creates another puzzle.

The resolution of some of these puzzles may have to do with something else entirely. Let me draw your attention to another survey of health in England. This is called *Health in England, 1998*, with the subtitle *Investigating the links between social inequalities and health.*[10] Although with a very similar title, it appears to have no connection with the *Health survey for England* undertaken by the National Centre for Social Research to which I have already referred. This one is produced by the Office of National Statistics for the Health Education Authority and is part of a series of studies known as the Health Education Monitoring Survey.

This 1998 survey interviewed 5816 adults, randomly selected from households that were themselves randomly selected. As well as asking questions relating to self-reported health and limiting long-standing illness, it asked questions relating to smoking, drinking, physical activity, diet, demographic and socio-economic factors and – of particular interest for our purposes – personal support and 'social capital'.

Social capital is a fashionable concept and, like most such concepts, rarely rigorously defined. Robert Puttnam, the originator of the idea, defined it as 'the features of social life – networks, norms and trust – that enable participants to act together more effectively to pursue shared objectives', an interpretation that does not immediately seem of direct relevance to individual health.[11] However, several authors have applied it to health, where the idea seems to be that an individual's sense of well-being is directly related to the extent of social support which he or she possesses and the extent of his or her civic engagement. Attempts to operationalise this idea have referred to a wide variety of factors, including social connections (family and friends), participation in the local community, the perceived extent of control over one's life, perceptions of quality of life in the community, income inequality and personal feelings of trust and safety.[12,13,14,15,16,17,18,19]

A specific example is the *Health in England* survey. It tried to gauge the extent of social connections by asking respondents how many people they felt they could turn to for help or comfort in a personal crisis. It examined participation in the local community by asking questions concerning respondents' involvement in community activities such as adult education, voluntary groups or local religious activities. It also asked questions relating to respondents' satisfaction with the amount of control they had over decisions that affect their lives, and with the extent of the influence that they felt they had over decisions that affected their neighbourhood. And it explored questions relating to what the Report termed 'neighbourhood social capital', including whether respondents enjoyed living in their neighbourhood, whether they felt safe there, whether neighbours looked after each other and whether there were good facilities for transport and leisure. Finally, the Survey also assigned an area deprivation score to each respondent.

The Survey found that, among the conventional socio-economic factors, age, household income, economic activity, and housing tenure were all important factors associated with self-reported health. However, they also found some of the indicators of social capital also to be significant, including satisfaction with control over life and neighbourhood social capital measures were positively linked with health. But community activity and control over decisions affecting the neighbourhood had no independent effect. Nor, perhaps surprisingly, did the area deprivation category, probably because it was swamped by the effect of individual indicators of deprivation.

That some aspects of social capital are closely related to self-reported health (although, interestingly enough, not always the same ones) is reinforced by other work in the area. Mitchell and colleagues, using data from the 'Health and Lifestyle Survey', found a link between self-reported health and people's attitude towards the community in which they lived, even after standard socio-economic factors that might also affect that link were taken into account.[15] Gatrell and colleagues, in an intensive study of four localities, correlated self-reported health with loneliness (inversely), connections with family and friends, access to facilities, and participation in the local community (all positively).[13]

Now some care has to be taken with these results because the direction of causation is not clear. Put simply, do low levels of social capital create poor health or does poor health affect social capital? It is clear that being in poor health will create difficulties in accessing such social capital as is available: going to adult education activities, doing voluntary work, even engaging in social activities are all more difficult if one is not feeling well. Even attitudes towards the community can be affected by one's state of health. In much of this work the question of direction of causation remains unresolved.

So what does this suggest about our various puzzles? One explanation for the relatively poor levels of health reported in cities (as distinct from the actual levels of health) could be because of a relative absence of social capital in urban areas. Unfortunately, none of the studies that I was able to unearth had any data on urban/rural comparisons, but it does not seem implausible to suppose that rural communities have rather more social capital than cities, however the latter is measured.

In support of the proposition that urban areas may lack key elements of social capital, let me draw your attention to some research being conducted by Ruth Lupton at my own institution, the Centre for Analysis of Social Exclusion (CASE) at the London School of Economics.[20] This is exploring in detail twelve of the poorest areas in Britain, the vast majority of which are urban. Interviews with GPs and other health professionals in the areas identified a number of specific health problems including cardiovascular disease, lung cancer and especially mental health. The last arises partly because some of these areas have high concentrations of people with severe mental illness, and partly because of widespread depression. This depression was often associated with a low sense of individual self-esteem and a sense of powerlessness.

The importance of powerlessness as a factor affecting individuals living in these areas was emphasised time and time again by interviewees. On occasion this was linked explicitly to health. A Health Action Zone project manager said:

> *People live shorter and more unhealthy lives in places like [x estate]. Levels of self-worth and self-esteem are low, so people do not look after their health. They have no control over their own lives or their environment. It is all about choice, but they do not have that – so, heart disease and cancer are high because no-one takes control of their lives. Social exclusion is all about choice.*

So where does this leave us in considering health and the city? First, we must be careful about mythologies. City dwellers often have an image of the country as full of rustic, clean-living communities peopled by apple-cheeked cottagers, not wealthy in material goods but rich in areas where it really counts, such as their health. In fact, this seems quite wrong: rural areas seem actually to be wealthier in terms of material goods but not necessarily better off in terms of actual health. Moreover, while they are more clean living in terms of smoking, the same is not true with respect to alcohol or diet.

But they do *report* better health. And this raises a puzzle about the factors affecting self-reported health: could there be factors associated with urban living that depress self-reported health relative to actual health? Although we have no data to make direct comparisons, I have suggested that there may be such factors and that they could perhaps be associated with the rather ill-defined notion of social capital. Certainly the evidence suggests that the lack of some forms of social capital are closely associated with a low self-assessment of health; and it seems quite plausible to suppose that the relevant forms of social capital – such as those associated with a sense of community – are more likely to be found in the country than in cities. This is an area ripe for future research.

However, studies of the links between social capital and health in poor urban areas suggest that the issue is more general than simply one of trying to explain differences between actual and reported health in urban and rural areas. It seems very likely that at least in those poor areas, if not in the wider city, indicators of social capital are linked with actual health as well as with self-reported health. It is also likely that the links go both ways: that poor health may contribute to poor social capital and as well as the other way round.

As I have indicated, social capital is a fuzzy concept and, if we are to go very much further in examining its links with health – actual or self-reported, in cities or in rural areas – it needs to be substantially refined. But I do believe that it is drawing our attention to factors that have been relatively neglected in many of the studies that examine the relationship between socio-economic factors associated with health. In particular, I have been impressed by the relationship between people's sense of powerlessness in poor urban areas and their health. Perhaps the future of health in these areas – and indeed the future of the health in cities in general – lies in linking health with empowerment. Better health empowers people, and empowering people gives them better health.

Acknowledgements

As I have indicated, this is a new area of investigation for me and I am very grateful to the following people for guiding my first fumbling steps. Judith Littlewood drew my attention to the puzzle with which this lecture opens. Roger Jowell and Rebecca Teers of the National Centre for Social Research kindly supplied with me with the unpublished data from the 1998 *Health survey for England*. Ruth Lupton provided invaluable bibliographical assistance and discussion of some of the issues.

Appendix

Table A.1 *Health survey for England:* health data

Percentages of adults
Reporting good or very good health

	Urban	Suburban	Rural	Total
Men	70	75	78	75
Women	69	73	77	73

Reporting limiting long-standing illness

Men	41	45	44	44
Women	43	45	41	44

Diagnosed with cardiovascular disease

Men	27	28	28	28
Women	26	28	29	28

Source: Health survey for England, 1998. Data supplied by the National Centre for Social Research.

Table A.2 *Health survey for England:* socio-demographic data

Percentages of adults
By income quintile

		Urban	Suburban	Rural	Total
Men	bottom quintile	29	17	14	18
	top quintile	20	20	22	20
Women	bottom quintile	28	20	16	20
	top quintile	18	17	20	18

By social class

		Urban	Suburban	Rural	Total
Men	I and II professional and managerial	34	36	45	38
	IV and V semi- and unskilled manual	24	19	18	20
Women	I and II professional and managerial	32	33	43	35
	IV and V semi- and unskilled manual	26	22	20	27

In selected age groups

	Urban	Suburban	Rural	Total
Men under 16	24	21	20	21
Men 65+	11	15	18	15
Women under 16	17	18	16	17
Women 65+	16	18	18	18

Source: Health survey for England, 1998. Data supplied by the National Centre for Social Research.

References

1. Department of Health. *Health survey for England. Cardiovascular disease '98.* London: HMSO, 1999.
2. *Ibid.*, 28. Respondents who reported having a particular condition were also asked if they had had it in the last 12 months, with the exception of high blood pressure (where they were asked if they still had it and if they were taking medication for it) and diabetes (where it was assumed that the condition was chronic and irreversible). No attempt was made to assess these self-reported diagnoses objectively. The Report notes that high blood pressure and diabetes are generally considered to be predisposing factors and not cardiovascular conditions *per se.*
3. In fact, some geographical data are included in the Report but they are classified in a way that does not readily permit any comparisons between cities and other geographical entities.
4. Denham C, White I. Differences in urban and rural Britain. *Population Trends* 1998; 91: 23–34.
5. The English figures are noticeably lower than the figures for both urban and rural areas reported in the *Health survey for England.* They do refer to different years, 1991 and 1998; this was a seven-year period during which, according to the General Household Survey, reported limiting long-standing illness has increased on average. But the most likely explanation for the difference is that they are simply referring to different things: one the proportion of adults reporting limiting long-standing illness, the other, the proportion of residents in households with a long-standing illness.
6. Victor Rodwin, in his contribution to this volume, provides an excellent overview of the relevant literature.
7. Whitehead M. Life and death over the Millennium. In: Drever F, Whitehead M, editors. *Health inequalities.* ONS Series DS No.15. London: HMSO, 1998.
8. Holland W, Stewart S. *Public health: the vision and the challenge.* London: The Nuffield Trust, 1997: Chapter 1.
9. There is evidence that mental health problems are worse in cities. A 1995 survey found depressive disorders, generalised anxiety and phobias are higher in urban than in rural areas. See Meltzer H, Gill B, Pettigrew M, Hinds K. *The prevalence of psychiatric morbidity among adults living in private households.* London: HMSO, 1995. See also Goldberg D, Thornicroft G, editors. *Mental health in our future cities.* London: Psychology Press, 1998.
10. Office of National Statistics. *Health in England 1998: investigating the links between social inequalities and health.* London: HMSO, 2000.
11. Puttnam R D. *Making democracy work: civic traditions in modern Italy.* Princeton: Princeton University Press, 1995.
12. Cooper H, Arber S, Fee L, Ginn J. *The influence of social support and social capital on health.* London: Health Education Authority, 1999.
13. Gatrell A, Thomas C, Bennett S, Bostock L, Popay J, Williams G, Shatahmasebi S. Understanding health inequalities: locating people in geographical and social spaces. In: Graham H, ed. *Understanding health inequalities.* Buckingham: Open University Press, 2000.

14. Bulle J. *Measuring social capital in five communities*. CACOM Working Paper Series No. 41. Sydney: Centre for Australian Community Organisation and Management (CACOM), University of Technology, 1998.

15. Mitchell R, Gleave S, Bartley M, Wiggins D, Joshi H. Do attitude and area influence health? A multilevel approach to health inequalities. *Health & Place* 2000; 6: 67–79.

16. Campbell C. *Social capital and health*. London: Health Education Authority, 1999.

17. Kawachi I *et al.* Social capital, income and inequality. *American Journal of Public Health* 1997; 87: 1491–98.

18. Wilkinson R. *Unhealthy societies: the afflictions of inequalities*. London: Routledge, 1996.

19. James N. *Nottingham Social Action Research Project (SARP) baseline survey: report to Nottingham health authority*. Nottingham: University of Nottingham, Division of Public Health Medicine and Epidemiology, 2000.

20. Lupton R. *Places apart? Findings from twelve disadvantaged areas. The initial report of the CASE area study*. CASE Report No. 14. London: Centre for Analysis of Social Exclusion (CASE), London School of Economics, 2001.

Chapter 13

Health in the city (2)

Victor G Rodwin

Urban health: is the city infected?

The city is, at once a centre for disease and poor health, and also a place for hope, cures and good health. From the earliest times, the city has attracted the poor and been the target of the plague, as well as war. Likewise, the health care industry has always been part of the economic base of cities – from Lourdes, in France, to Rochester, Minnesota, to megacities around the world. With its highly disproportionate share of health resources, e.g. hospitals, physicians, nurses and social services, the big city is a centre of excellence in medicine. Yet, as Richard Horton, editor of the *Lancet* once noted: 'for all of its rational efficiency and benevolent intent, the city is likely to be the death of us.'[1] Are cities socially infected breeding grounds for disease? Or do they represent critical spatial entities for promotion of population health?

I propose to begin with a global view of urban health and disease, and the challenge this poses for public health today. Next, I examine some evidence for the hypothesis that population health in cities is relatively poor. Finally, I suggest that the more pertinent question is not whether the city is unhealthy or healthy but rather the extent to which we can alleviate the problems posed by inequalities of income and wealth – in the city as well as outside of it.

A global view of urban health

The United Nations projects that 61 per cent of humanity will live in cities by 2025.[2] There are now 19 megacities; in 2015, the UN estimates that there will be 23.[3] The fastest growing megacities are located in developing nations. Such cities are like 'huge human sponges, soaking up 61 million new people each year'.[4] Air travel and other routes of transportation have magnified their influence and vulnerability.

In contrast to megacities in developing countries, New York, London, Paris and Tokyo – the largest cities of wealthy nations belonging to the OECD – share a recent history of relative success in assuring their population's health, and confront a range of common characteristics and problems. They are great centres for prestigious university hospitals, medical schools and medical research institutions. Despite these resources and the success of their public health reformers and urban planners in improving their quality of life, these world cities still confront onerous health risks – albeit to different degrees – for at least six problems:

- the re-emergence of infectious diseases (e.g. tuberculosis) and the arrival of new ones (e.g. AIDS)
- water and air pollution
- an increase in the homeless population
- barriers in access to medical services for ethnic minorities and/or the poor
- terrorism (e.g. the World Trade Center bombing in New York) and bio-terrorism (e.g. the release of toxic sarin gas in Tokyo's subway system)
- rising inequalities among social groups.

These problems will challenge any big city to develop a solid public health infrastructure. With or without such investments, there is already widespread belief that urban health is not as good as that of the population as a whole. Those who disagree point to contrary evidence. Strangely enough, there is insufficient evidence to provide strong support for either view. Hence, the 'puzzles' to which Julian Le Grand has alluded.

The reason we have so little solid evidence is that we have no routine information systems for monitoring the health of populations living in cities. While institutions responsible for disease surveillance and control – at the international, national and local authority levels – collect vital statistics and epidemiologic data by geographic location, national policy is made without systematic analysis of information for monitoring health status, public health infrastructure and the performance of health systems in cities. Julian Le Grand is deceptively modest when he confesses to 'knowing relatively little about health and the city'. The fact is that all of us know relatively little because information on health status is reported routinely by national or regional units; the city is most often ignored as a unit of analysis in health policy. I therefore propose to present a case for both sides of the urban health controversy – the city is sick and the city is healthy – summarising highly selective evidence for each view.

The sick city

Since the city is, by definition, the place where human density is greatest, it is hardly surprising that the city is a vector for disease transmission, particularly for the spread of infectious disease. One has only to recall the vivid descriptions of the plague in

Egypt or the cholera epidemics in London or New York or Paris to realise how cities can become epicentres for disease. But beyond such images of epidemics in the city, what kind of evidence do we actually have on population health in cities of OECD nations?

The Big Cities Health Inventory in the United States

In 1997, an unusual and unpublished database was assembled in the United States by the Chicago Department of Health.[5] Data reported by health departments of 46 big cities in the US (between 1992 and 1994) indicated that the average incidence rates for the leading infectious diseases – tuberculosis, AIDS and syphilis – were much higher in these cities than for the US as a whole. This is to be expected given the effects of population density on the transmission of infectious disease. More striking, however, were the mortality data (1994) reported by these cities for the leading causes of death from non-communicable diseases: heart disease and cancer. In stark contrast to the situation in England, the average age-adjusted mortality rate from heart disease across these cities was higher than the US average – 164 per 100,000 population versus 145.[6] For cancer, the average age-adjusted mortality rate across these cities was 153 per 100,000 population, in contrast to 132 for the US as a whole.

There are two convenient ways to summarise this information. The first is to calculate an overall mortality rate for all causes of death; the second is to calculate years of potential life lost (YLL). For all of the criticisms one might make of the YLL measure, it is nonetheless an important indicator of the health of a population. Simply defined, it is the number of years of life lost by people who died before the age of 65. The overall mortality rate for the 46 cities was 654 per 100,000; for the US as a whole it was 507. The average years of potential life lost for the 46 cities was 75 per 1000 population; for the US as a whole it was 54.

Urban social health in the United States (1995)

In 1995, the National Association of Public Hospitals in the US published a compendium of data on the 100 largest cities.[7] Among a range of indicators, this report notes that, in 1993, the gonorrhoea rate in the 25 largest cities was 434 per 100,000; for the US as a whole it was 172 per 100,000. Shifting to more generalised health indicators, the average infant mortality rate for the 100 cities was 12.2 per 1000 in 1988; for the US as a whole it was 9.8. In a subsequent study more specifically on 'inner city health', Dennis Andrulis, the former Director of Research for the National Association of Public Hospitals, characterises the greater prevalence of a large number of health problems in cities than in suburbs and rural areas as the 'urban health penalty'.[8]

In support of these findings on the urban health penalty and in contrast to evidence from the survey in England (see Le Grand's chapter), a study of low birth weight and children's height in England's Northumberland County concludes that 'there is substantial disadvantage to living in urban areas compared with rural areas'. This finding is particularly noteworthy because it adjusts for levels of 'deprivation' across urban and rural areas.[9] Yet another study, in Wales, using a different indicator of 'health' – premature mortality from all causes – also supports the sick city hypothesis after controlling for differences in 'deprivation' measures across urban and rural areas.[10] What then should one conclude from this assorted evidence on health in cities? People don't just 'feel worse' in cities (as indicated by the survey cited by Le Grand) – they are doing worse. Cities are therefore unhealthy places – at least in the US, England and Wales. What about in the rest of the EC?

Project Megapoles: health in Europe's capitals

Project Megapoles, a study of Europe's capital cities, has generated some fascinating comparative data. Funded by the EEC, this project seeks to improve health in these cities, especially for three target groups:

- youth and young families
- the socially disadvantaged
- older persons

In its main report, Project Megapoles compares age-specific mortality for each European capital to national rates.[11] Once again, we have, for the most part, evidence in support of the 'sick city' hypothesis. On average, mortality rates for infants (0–4 years) were 7 per cent higher in the cities than in their respective nations (31 per cent higher in Copenhagen; 44 per cent higher in Vienna; only 6 per cent higher in London and Stockholm). In contrast, these rates were lower in five cities: Helsinki (–18 per cent), Lisbon (–9 per cent), Lazio (–12 per cent), Madrid (–20 per cent) and Lyon (–25 per cent).

The World Cities Project

The Megapoles project was a source of inspiration in designing our own World Cities Project, a collaborative enterprise between the Wagner School of Public Service, New York University, and the International Longevity Center (ILC-USA). Among the megacities of the world today, New York, Paris, London and Tokyo often serve as a model for their counterparts in developing nations due to their relative wealth and dominance, their ties to the global economy, and their concentration of business, cultural and scientific activities. Along with our partners at ILC-UK, ILC-France and ILC-Japan, we have embarked on a project to study public health infrastructure as well as health outcomes and health services for older persons and children in these cities.[12] The evidence we have examined so far lends some qualified support for the hypothesis that population health in cities is worse than at the national level. I emphasise the term 'qualified' because the evidence is mixed (see Table 13.1). In NYC, the evidence is incontrovertible: life expectancy at birth (LEB) is lower than in the US as a whole, particularly for males (67.8 years); infant mortality (IM) is higher; and rates of 'feeling worse' (self-reported total mobility limitations) among persons of 65 years and older (18.1 per cent) are higher than for New York State overall (16 per cent). In Tokyo, however, there are no significant differences, along these measures, in comparison to Japan as a whole. In Paris, although there are no differences in LEB when compared to France as a whole, infant mortality is lower in Paris than in France as a whole (4.0 versus 4.6). And in London, although there are no significant differences in IM, or in LEB for men, women have a longer LEB (79.3) than in the UK as a whole (78.8).

This 'qualified support' is fractured, however, when one examines life expectancy at 65 years, particularly for women (see Table 13.2). In New York City and London, there are no differences between city and the nation. In Tokyo, however, women live longer at 65 than in Japan as a whole (21.2 years versus 20.9 years). And in Paris, women live much longer than in France as a whole (26.5 versus 20.6).

Such findings – however intriguing – do not refute the hypothesis that cities are unhealthy, for the strongest case has yet to be made. It is that these wealthy world cities, along with all other megacities, are places where flagrant inequalities exist among sub-population groups. All of the averages we have considered mask enormous pockets of poverty with disadvantaged groups that suffer disproportionately in terms of their health status.

The healthy city

Since the city has been a symbol of civilization and human accomplishment over the past 2000 years and earlier, it has been the place for visions of human betterment, including population health.[13] In 1875, Sir Benjamin Ward Richardson, a disciple of Edwin Chadwick, gave a lecture to the Social Science Association meeting in Brighton, England on *Hygeia: a city of health*. His vision of an ideally healthy city inspired Ebenezer Howard and the 'Garden City' movement of the 1890s, as well as the WHO's 'Healthy Cities' movement that began in the late 1980s.[14]

Moving from the vision to the concept, the case for the healthy city is typically grounded in economic arguments or celebrations of its vitality and innovation in such diverse realms as architecture, urban design, culture, technology, and more. A recent American example may be found in President Clinton's State of the Union message in 1998, in which he refers to American cities as the 'vibrant hubs of great metropolitan regions'. In this respect, the Report of the US Conference of Mayors and the National Association of Counties notes that, between 1982 and 1998, metropolitan areas in the United States generated 85 per cent of all jobs and 86 per cent of the nation's total economic growth.[15] This economic power is concentrated among some regional giants that dwarf not only their own states but most of the world's nations. Metropolitan New York's economic output, for example, is greater than that of 45 of the 50 states.[16]

Claims for the enduring power of cities, including big cities, most often come out of the literature on urban planning and do not typically invoke evidence about population health. But there is a body of evidence in support of the hypothesis that urban health compares favourably to that of the nation as a whole.

The National Health Interview Survey

The National Health Interview Survey (NHIS) is one of the most reliable indicators of functional health (how people feel) in the United States. In 1988, the results of this national survey were reported for major metropolitan regions in the US. Comparison of health indicators for these regions – an aggregation of the urban population – with the national average provides a unique opportunity to shed light on another dimension of urban health (see Table 13.3). In contrast to the Big Cities Health Inventory, which relies on outcome measures of health, NHIS suggests that most indicators of self-assessed health status are better in major metropolitan areas than for the country as a whole.

For example, the percentage of population with activity limitations is lower in metropolitan areas than in the country as whole (12.4 in MSAs versus 13.7). Likewise, the percentage of population reporting fair or poor health in the metropolitan areas is lower than in the country as a whole (8.7 versus 9.4). Also, the number of restricted activity days per 100 persons is lower in metropolitan areas than in the rest of the country (1390 days versus 1470 days). Self-reported data on selected chronic conditions support these more general indicators of functional health in the NHIS (see Table 13.3). There are only two conditions for which reported rates appear to be higher in major metropolitan areas than in the US as a whole: asthma and deformities or orthopaedic impairments.

Focused studies on urban–rural differences

In Virginia, a study of low birth-weight infants in rural versus urban areas found that rural areas had a higher incidence of low birth-weight infants.[17] This study probably reflects the fact that the infants' parents in rural areas were more apt to be single, less educated, African-American, and to have lower income than their counterparts in the urban areas.

In Kentucky, a comparison of health status between rural and urban adults found few differences when measured by a sophisticated set of criteria used in the 'medical outcomes study' (physical functioning, role functioning, social functioning, general mental health and general health perceptions). With respect to rural versus urban elderly adults, however, Mainous and Kohrs found a situation of 'rural inferiority' – rural elderly had significantly worse health status than their urban counterparts.[18]

In Georgia, with respect to cancer, a study found that residents of a rural area were twice as likely to have unstaged cancers as their urban counterparts. This probably reflects less effective diagnosis and assessment of the tumours' growth. Among patients with a known and documented tumour 'stage' at diagnosis, rural patients tended to have more advanced disease than urban patients, which probably reflects better access to medical treatment in urban areas.[19] Thus, for cancer care there may be an urban 'advantage' at least in terms of treatment.

Additional and more recent evidence from the NHIS (beyond Table 13.3) suggests that the central city is healthier with respect to self-reported incidence of diabetes and hypertension. Also, as in England, the US National Household Survey of Drug Abuse reports higher rates of binge drinking and consumption of alcohol in rural areas than in urban areas. But in contrast to England, the US has higher tobacco use in rural areas than in cities. In summary, a review of selective evidence can support the hypothesis that cities are actually healthy in comparison to rural areas.

Concluding observations

There is evidence of an 'urban penalty' in terms of doing worse and feeling worse in the United States. But there is also evidence of an 'urban advantage' in terms of self-assessed health status, health habits and with respect to quality cancer screening services. The reason the evidence reviewed here is mixed and possibly confusing is twofold:

(a) There are many ways to define and measure health. As we have seen, measures range from disease prevalence, LEB, age-specific mortality rates and indicators of self-assessed health.

(b) There are many ways to define and measure cities. As we have seen, spatial definitions range from inner cities to large metropolitan areas. Therefore, an apt conclusion may be that the *a priori* is as dangerous in health policy as it is in philosophy! More concretely, this suggests that in thinking about rural versus urban health, it is prudent to avoid assumptions about the validity of urban versus rural factors as determinants of health and to include well-known risk factors for bad health as they affect both rural and urban spatial units. These factors are: poverty, inequality and low levels of social capital/social cohesion.

Acknowledgements

I wish to thank Irena Dushi, Susan Ghanbarpour and Meron Makonnen for their assistance with my review of the literature and preparation of tables for this paper.

Table 13.1 Life expectancy, infant mortality and total mobility limitation, national and city data

Location	LEB (male)	LEB (female)	IM (1995)
New York City (1990)	67.8	77.7	8.8
US	71.8	78.8	8.0
Tokyo (23 wards) (1995)	76.3	82.9	4.2
Japan	76.4	82.9	4.3
Paris (1990)	72.6	80.8	4.0
France	72.7	80.9	4.9
London (1991)	73.1	79.3	6.3
UK	73.2	78.8	6.0

Sources

Life Expectancy at Birth (LEB):

New York City: New York City Department of Health (NYCDOH)/Center for Health Statistics.

Paris: INSEE, *Chiffres et Indicateurs départementaux*, published by Ministère de la Santé and Ministère des Affaires Sociales.

Tokyo: Tokyo Eiseikyoku (1997). *Annual report on health in Tokyo.* Vol. 48. Tokyo Statistical Association, 1997.

London: Life expectancy figures come from Bone *et al. Health expectancy and its uses.* OPCS, April 1995.

US, Japan, France and UK: figures come from *OECD health data 2000: a comparative analysis of 29 countries.*

Infant Mortality (IM):

New York City: New York City Department of Health (NYCDOH)/Center for Health Statistics.

Paris: INSEE, *Chiffres et Indicateurs départementaux*, published by Ministère de la Santé and Ministère des Affaires Sociales.

Tokyo: Tokyo Eiseikyoku (1997). *Annual report on health in Tokyo.* Vol. 48. Tokyo Statistical Association, 1997.

London: Infant mortality figures come from PHCDS.

US, Japan, France and UK: figures come from *OECD health data 2000: a comparative analysis of 29 countries.*

Table 13.2 Life expectancy at 65 years

Location	Life expectancy at 65 years (male)	Life expectancy at 65 years (female)
New York City (1990)	15.3	19.0
US	15.1	18.9
Tokyo (23 wards) (1995)	16.5	21.1
Japan	16.5	20.9
Paris (1995)	21.4	26.2
France	16.1	20.6
London (1991)	14.5	18.6
UK	14.2	18.0

Sources

New York City: New York City Department of Health (NYCDOH)/Center for Health Statistics.

Paris: INSEE, *Chiffres et Indicateurs départementaux*, published by Ministère de la Santé and Ministère des Affaires Sociales.

Tokyo: Tokyo Eiseikyoku (1997). *Annual report on health in Tokyo. Vol. 48.* Tokyo Statistical Association, 1997.

London: Life expectancy figures come from Bone *et al. Health expectancy and its uses.* OPCS, April 1995.

US, Japan, France and UK: figures come from OECD *health data 2000: a comparative analysis of 29 countries.*

Table 13.3 Selected health characteristics

Health characteristics	All large CMSAs & MSAs[a]	Rest of the country
Percentage limited in activity	12.4	13.7
Percentage with fair or poor respondent-assessed health	8.7	9.4
Restricted activity days per 100 persons	1389.8	1470
Arthritis	113.1	129.9
Deafness	71	90.8
Deformities or orthopaedic impairments	121.6	111.6
Heart disease	71.6	84.1
High blood pressure	108.2	121.5
Haemorrhoids	43.6	45.8
Chronic bronchitis	46.2	49.4
Asthma	44	41.2
Hay fever	88.6	93
Chronic sinusitis	114.2	139.7

Sources

US data from *Current estimates from NHIS 1988, Series 10, # 173*. CMSA and MSA data from *Health characteristics of large metropolitan statistical areas: US, 1988–1989*

Notes

a. MSAs are metropolitan statistical areas. The NHIS report contains data for 18 Consolidated Metropolitan Statistical Areas (CMSAs) and 15 (MSAs). The total population represented in the survey is 117,211,000. The definition and titles of MSAs are established by the US Office of Management and Budget (OMB) with the advice of the Federal Committee on Metropolitan Statistical Areas. Since January 1980, each MSA must include at least one of the following: one city with 50,000 or more inhabitants and an area (defined by the US Bureau of the Census as urbanised) of at least 50,000 inhabitants and a total MSA population of at least 100,000 (75,000 in New England). The 1980 standards provide that, within metropolitan complexes of 1 million or more population, separate component areas are defined if specified criteria are met. Such areas are designated primary metropolitan statistical areas (PMSAs), and any area containing PMSAs is designated a consolidated metropolitan statistical area (CMSA).

References

1. Horton R. The infected metropolis. *Lancet* 1998; 347 (8995): 134–35.
2. Linden D. The exploding cities of the developing world. *Foreign Affairs* 1996; 75: 1
3. UN, Department of Economic and Social Information and Policy Analysis, 1995.
4. Horton R. *Ibid.*
5. *Big cities health inventory, 1997: the health of urban USA.* City of Chicago, Department of Public Health.
6. See Le Grand's paper for English data.
7. *Urban social health.* Washington, DC: National Association of Public Hospitals, 1995.
8. Andrulis D P. The urban health penalty: new dimensions and directions in inner-city health care. In: *Inner city health care.* Philadelphia, PA: American College of Physicians, 1997.
9. Reading R, Raybould S, Jarvis S. Deprivation, low birth weight, and children's height: a comparison between rural and urban areas. *BMJ* 1993; 307 (6917): 1458–62.
10. Senior M, Williams H, Higgs G. Urban–rural mortality differentials: controlling for material deprivation. *Social Science & Medicine* 2000; 51: 289–305.
11. *Health in Europe's capitals* (www.megapoles.org), 30.
12. Rodwin V G. Population aging and longevity in world cities. *CGP Newsletter.* Japan Foundation Center for Global Partnership (www.cgp.org/cgplink)
13. Hall P. *Cities in civilization.* New York: Pantheon, 1998.
14. Hancock T. The evolution, impact and significance of the Healthy Cities/Healthy Communities movement. *Journal of Public Health Policy,* Spring 1993.
15. *The state of the nation's cities.* Washington, DC: Department of Housing and Urban Development, 1998.
16. *Ibid.*
17. Alexy B, Nichols B, Heverly M A, Garzon L. Prenatal factors and birth outcomes in the public health service: a rural/urban comparison. *Research in Nursing & Health* 1997; 20: 61–70.
18. Mainous III A G, Kohrs F P. A comparison of health status between rural and urban adults. *Journal of Community Health* 1995; 20 (5): 423–31.
19. Liff J M, Chow W C, Greenberg R S. Rural–urban differences in stage at diagnosis: possible relationship to cancer screening. *Cancer* 1991; 1; 1 March.